DYING WITH
JOY AND SORROW

True Stories
From the Bedside
of the Dying

Judy Voss RN and Linda Neider RN
Illustrations by Kate Parker RN

E-O-L Publishing

...learning to live at the end-of-life

The true stories contained in this book may seem familiar to many of our readers. However, details and names have been changed when requested to honor the privacy of all involved.

Library of Congress Cataloging-in-Publication Data:
Dying with Joy and Sorrow: True Stories from the Bedside of the Dying
Co-authors: Judy Voss and Linda Neider
Illustrations by Kate Parker
Cover design by Nikki Griffin

E-O-L Publishing, P.O. Box 1341, New Smyrna Beach, Fl 32170
© 2004 by Judy Voss, Linda Neider, Kate Parker

ISBN 0-9753705-0-2

Printed in the United States of America by Express Printing, DeLand, Florida.

The authors gratefully acknowledge the following publishers who have given permission to share their words with you.

A Different Drummer: My Thirty Years With Ronald Reagan, by Michael Deaver, with a foreword by Nancy Reagan, excerpt from page 213. Copyright © 2001 by Michael Deaver. Reprinted by permission of HarperCollins Publishers Inc.
Angels Along The Way, by Della Reese, Berkeley Publishing Co, member of Penguin Putnam, Cover Design by Isabella Fasciano, Front Cover photo by Michael Grecco, Copyright © 1997
I Almost Remember from *Oh Pray My Wings Are Gonna Fit Me Well,* by Maya Angelou, copyright © 1975 by Maya Angelou. Used by permission of Random House, Inc.
Intimate Death: How the Dying Teach Us How to Live, by Marie de Hennezel, Used by permission of Publisher Random House, Inc./Alfred a. Knopft Inc., Copyright © 1997
I Shall Not Be Moved, by Maya Angelou. *"Ailey, Baldwin, Floyd, Killens, and Mayfield",* copyright © 1990 by Maya Angelou, Used by permission of Random House, Inc.
Life Lessons, by Elisabeth Kubler-Ross and David Kessler. Reprinted with permission of Scribner, an imprint of Simon & Schuster Adult Publishing Group. Copyright © 2000 by Elisabeth Kubler-Ross Family Limited Partnership and David Kessler, Inc.
Michael Landon: His Triumph and Tragedy, by Aileen Joyce, copyright © 1991. Published by Kensington Publishing Corp.
Michael Landon: Life, Love & Laughter, by Harry Flynn and Pamela Flynn, copyright © 1991. Used by permission of Pomegranate Press, Ltd.
Ordinary Grace, by Kathleen A. Brehoney, copyright © 1999 by Kathleen A. Brehoney. Used by permission of Riverhead Books, an imprint of Penguin Group (USA) Inc.

Dedication

*It is with heartfelt thankfulness
that we dedicate this book
to our Hospice of Volusia/Flagler patients
from the past, the present, and the future,
and to their loved ones.
It is our hope that your memories of joy
will far outweigh those of sorrow.*

Judy Voss and Linda Neider

Foreword

Heart wrenching to heartfelt, joyful to fearful, marvelous to mysterious, all describe the stories within these pages. From front porches to Florida beaches, to flower gardens and chapels, you will visit many patients along with their families and discover how joy was found in their sorrow as death drew near. After reading stories about rising spirits, visitors from Heaven, visions beyond normal explanation, and how others coped with caring for the dying, the fear associated with the end of life can be diminished and peace and comfort found in the moment.

In our society we celebrate and honor bravery. I wish to honor the bravest people on earth...those facing the end of life and those who care for them. Caregivers of the dying patient are ordinary people doing extraordinary things. Their courageous feats of love have blossomed into these stories and I thank them all for this gift.

Many people have written the stories in *Dying with Joy and Sorrow: True Stories from the Bedside of the Dying*. These stories you are about to read have been written by: children, spouses, moms, dads, grandmas and grandpas, daughters, sons, nurses, volunteers, home health aides, social workers, hospice staff, loved ones and friends. Yet, none of the stories could have been authored without the patient. With deep respect and gratitude we acknowledge their sacrifices and hope that they realized their impact on us.

Judy Voss RN and Linda Neider RN have brought this collection of heartfelt stories to life by authoring and compiling stories for this book. Kate Parker RN, using her artistic abilities through her gentle hands, brings visual beauty to these stories. For years they have tended to loved ones at the bedside of dying patients and witnessed their private journeys of joy and sorrow at the most intimate of times.

Debbie Harley, past Executive Director of Hospice of Volusia/Flagler, has a deep commitment and dedication to the hospice movement and has fully supported the publication of *Dying with Joy and Sorrow*. Her message of hospice is loud and clear in the stories you are about to read: "Live sweetly and honestly and with joy in your heart. Sorrow comes in great waves, but joy...joy is the wellspring of the fountain of youth!"

Fran Davis RN CHPN
Executive Director
Hospice of Volusia/Flagler

Contents

Introduction

Being Like A Goose

The cackle of honkers has always made listeners perk up and look to the sky! It is a majestic site to see the Canadian geese overhead, working together in their trek going north or south. When heard in the spring, those moments in time implied the long northern winter was coming to a close, hopefully!

The great thing about the honkers is how much we can be like them. As the geese move into their "V" formation, they help each other with the uplift of their wings, allowing for a much more efficient flight and preservation of energy. But when the lead goose tires, he relinquishes his position to one who has greater strength and endurance. This teamwork and sharing a common goal is extraordinary. Yet when a goose is ill and is forced to leave his place in the formation, two of his partners will leave their formation and follow the ill goose, staying with him until he is recovered or death occurs. What devotion, love and loyalty are exhibited in these graceful birds!

As humans, it would be a great benefit to the caregivers of the dying to relinquish some bedside duties to others, when one's resources and energies have been exhausted. There still could be plenty of honking and encouragement from throughout the home to cheer each and everyone on! Frequently, many family members and loved ones sacrifice their time and leave their own family and job responsibilities to be at the bedside of their loved one who is ill and dying.

What a beautiful sacrifice of love in caring for someone who is dying. This sacrifice is truly a privilege that not all are able to make because of extenuating circumstances or the fear of the unknown, which may cause a feeling of inadequacy. Hopefully, through *Dying with Joy and Sorrow*, any doubt or hesitation you have had in caring for your dying loved one will be diminished and you will become that special caregiver.

Kate Parker.

Butterfly Kisses – "The Last Wedding" from page 12

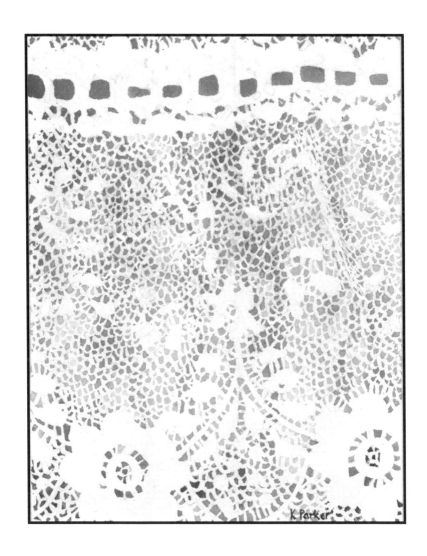

"I Thee Wed Three Times" from page 16

"Mom's Donuts" from page 15

From the Garden from page 22

Window Box Orchid from page 37

Sue's Ocean from page 24

"Visions and Phenomenal Senses" from page 33

Chapter One

Joy on the Mountain

Joy! Such a tiny word that is capable of holding one's most treasured memories! Great gladness, state of happiness, delight, glad praise or worship…which definition of joy describes how you felt when you experienced your mountain-top moments, the most precious and treasured of your memories?

Now think of that little word again and choose the definition that best describes how you want to feel as you or your loved one departs this earth. You believe that day of joy will never come because many in our society dictate we must be fearful of death. So how could anyone find joy in those memories? Someday, each of us may have to decide whether to view the dying process as fearful and dreadful or accept it and open our heart to the blessings and joy that can be found surrounding it.

One of the greatest joys of memory making while caring for the dying is being a part of the process called *Life Review*. Often, the dying and their loved ones will reflect back on their lives and share their burdens and/or blessings they carried together or as one. In addition, new stories evolve as they progress through the dying process. The following personal accounts of the joys and sorrows of losing loved ones are inspirational, thought provoking and illustrate the balance of life and death and joy and sorrow. These stories can shake you to your core or cause you to laugh until you cry. It is a great honor to be allowed inside these stories that are a very personal aspect of one's living, as one is dying! We sincerely hope you enjoy these reflective moments and gain strength and comfort from them.

The Last Wedding

Holly Van Hoose is a nurse who started her career as a volunteer with hospice. Through it all, her love of people remains constant, as you will see with this beautiful wedding story that she witnessed. You just may need a hanky before you have read it all.

The request came from Mr. Brown's primary hospice nurse and social worker for a very special need. Mr. Brown needed assistance preparing for and being tended to before, during and after the wedding of his youngest and last remaining daughter. The family had decided to advance the wedding to an earlier date because of Mr. Brown's terminal cancer and his 18-year-old daughter wanted him to be able to "give her away."

When I arrived at the patient's home there was a flurry of activities. Mom had things under control but she still wanted to make sure everything was perfect for her daughter. The patient lay in his hospital bed located by the front door in the living room where everyone who came had to walk right by him. He was very pale and weak, but aware of the celebratory air surrounding him.

Mom got ready and came out into the room to show her husband her new dress. He told her in a weak voice that she looked nice. She left the two of us so that she could prepare the wedding site, leaving me with the information I needed to care for Mr. Brown.

He needed a shave and a bed bath and to be dressed in a suit, complete with a boutonniere and shoes. As I was shaving him, I told him his face needed to be very smooth because I knew several women would be kissing him today. He smiled.

During this time, the bride and her sister arrived from having her hair done with the veil pinned in. One of her best friends and mother arrived to help her get dressed and then get ready themselves. The bride came into the living room to show her father how she looked, and said, "Daddy, do I look beautiful?"

He responded, "Yes, Sweetie, you do."

She came over and kissed him, rose up and turned away, wiping a tear from her eye. Then she left.

I had no privacy curtain to draw around Mr. Brown and people were coming and going, so it was a challenge to bathe him discreetly. He never seemed to mind any of it. Everything he did was done very slowly, as any amount of exertion tired him and caused him to perspire and be short of breath.

Finally, after a couple of hours he was ready to go. He then was taken in a wheelchair to his daughter's car so his son-in-law could drive him to the Elks Lodge, where the wedding and reception were to be held. I changed into my "wedding clothes" and followed them in my car.

When we arrived at the lodge, I took him in to greet some of his friends whom he hadn't seen in some time. Everyone was happy to see him. I handed him over to his son-in-law who took him over to the area where the wedding was to be performed. As the ceremony was about to begin, the bride appeared. She held her father's hand as his son-in-law pushed the wheelchair forward. He was able to give his daughter away. There was not a dry eye in the room. After the wedding and the dinner was the dance. The bride and groom danced the first dance and then the new groom went over to his new father-in-law, pushed his wheelchair to the new bride so Dad could hold hands and "dance" with his beautiful daughter to the song " Butterfly Kisses." Again the tears flowed.

Mr. Brown was tired after that and was ready to go home. We made a slow departure through the crowd of well-wishers to his sister's car where she and I helped him in and she drove him home, with me following. The rest of the family was able to stay as long as they wanted and his sister went back after we got Mr. Brown into the bed. I got him ready for bed and he slept until they returned home.

It was such a privilege to be a part of that joyous day full of love, happiness and memory making. How could anyone NOT love that kind of a job?

Gentle Reflections: Mr. Brown, his family and Holly were part of a magnificent plan that resulted in everlasting memories. This type of teamwork exhibited in a glorious celebration can provide a peaceful and contented passing.

Mom's Donuts

Sue Mossman provides Continuous Care Nursing for hospice patients, which is around the clock nursing care often needed as death becomes imminent. Here Sue shares a heart-warming story from her own neighborhood. It may make your mouth water and your eyes tear.

The need for Continuous Care Nursing was called in and I did the 4 pm-12 am shift for many days. The patient had periods of confusion and disorientation in between moments of great clarity. One afternoon after his kids had all arrived from out of state, the topic turned to Dad's favorite childhood recipes. "Mom's Donuts" was the winner! The patient had told us how great they tasted and how he had watched his mother make them so many times. Wouldn't it be great if they could be made now so we all could taste them?

The patient's wife had been searching closets, cookbooks and personal recipe files for some time and wasn't able to find the donut recipe. Since the patient was becoming increasingly confused, we doubted we would find it. Some time later during that shift, the patient woke up stating, "I know where it is!"

"It" turned out to be the long sought recipe! I was instructed to look in the closet near his bed in a certain colored folder for a yellow colored paper. I did so and there was the recipe!

By this time, the night shift was about to begin and the family had retired, so the patient and I discussed the recipe at length. When the night nurse arrived, the joy of the find was shared with her. During her shift she continued to delight in the childhood tales of the patient.

The next night she arrived with a plate of donuts for the patient and his family! Making donuts at home is a lost art in today's world but she did a credible job! The patient gave her some hints to fine-tune her new talent. The smile on his face was indescribable! He promised to judge her progress with each batch she promised to bring him but that first batch turned out to be the only one he tasted. We know he tasted the love!

Gentle Reflections: Often times our loved ones will prepare our favorite meal or dessert as an expression of their love for us. Unfortunately, when our physical bodies are ill, the amount of that gift of food one can consume is far less. The body can no longer process the foods or liquids once able, so the desire and taste for foods diminish. This is no reflection on the food or the loved one who prepared it, but rather a symptom of our loved one's illness progressing. Continue to prepare your loved one's favorite foods realizing that he will do his best to at least eat a small portion but may have to decide to only savor the moment of love exhibited.

I Thee Wed Three Times!

Joe, a man who was losing his wife Joyce in a valiant battle against cancer, put the following love story in writing for me, Judy. It is a huge honor for me to share in such precious and joyful memories as these. We laughed and we cried, especially when I heard Joe killed a five-foot rattlesnake with cucumbers after Joyce found it in their garden! Thanks, Joe.

When my wife Joyce and I were married, I didn't have a ring for her. I bought one not too long after though. She either lost that one in the toilet while washing a diaper for our second of five children or she lost it in a bag of coleslaw we were doing up.

With two small children in tow and my wife pregnant way out front, I insisted Joyce go across Woodland Boulevard in DeLand to a drugstore to help me buy some film for our camera so we could take pictures at our Christmas Eve celebration at Grandpa and Grandma's house. I then steered her into a jewelry store. A nice clerk greeted us and I told him we wanted to look at some wedding rings. That was the second time I married her.

Later, when Joyce went into the hospital for pancreatic cancer, she handed me her wedding band, which I put in my pocket and somehow lost. I later obtained an almost duplicate one with the help of one of our daughters, Marjorie, and married Joyce a third time with the words: "I thee wed!"

Gentle Reflections: The love and tenderness a couple has for each other can be exhibited in many ways as the end of life approaches! It is common to see a spouse, a child or grandchild lying next to their loved one as the moments of death approach. Words of thankfulness for the many years of love and laughter, and for being part of a beautiful family, are exchanged. I am privileged to witness and share in such tender moments. Please don't ever be afraid to be close to someone who is dying. That is their hour of greatest need, as it is yours. There is nothing to fear for love is a powerful blessed thing that binds us together.

Happy Birthday to You!

Joan Thomas tells her story about a very deep love between a husband and his wife that she witnessed while providing Continuous Care Nursing.

I have been asked many times, "How can you be a hospice nurse?" This story about Rosco is an example of why I feel privileged to be one.
I became Rosco's nurse the weekend of March 23, 2002. He had not had anything to eat for over two weeks and drank very little fluid. He was not expected to live through the weekend.
Rosco was paralyzed except for his right arm so he had worked out a communication system with his family. When he wiggled his right index finger or if he winked at them, they knew he was telling them he loved them.
On March 24 Rosco asked what the date was and we told him. That evening he requested water and continued to take small sips using his right hand and a sipper cup. The family got together and decided he must have remembered his wife Joyce's birthday, Wednesday, March 27th. Rosco never once mentioned the birthday. On Tuesday the 26th, Rosco's sons asked him if he would like them to get Joyce a birthday present from him. He asked them to get her roses.
I worked the 12 am–8 am shift on the morning of March 27th. Rosco had been awake all night. He had waved the angels off at his usual 3 am time and he was very content. Joyce got up at her usual 5:30 am time. She always came to his bedside to say, "good morning." Rosco looked up at her with the biggest brown eyes you have ever seen and started to sing:

*"Happy Birthday to You, Happy Birthday to You,
You are the love of my life,
Happy Birthday to You!"*

Then Rosco said, "I have waited all night to sing Happy Birthday to You!" Needless to say, we were all in tears. Rosco's sons assisted me with bathing him and dressing him in a bright shirt, which Joyce had picked out. I was told they celebrated all day.

When I returned at midnight, Rosco was awake and he told me, "Everything was perfect, just as I had hoped it would be. Now I am ready!"

Rosco's love for his family allowed him to stay with them until March 30th. The love I witnessed between this beautiful man and his family is something I will cherish forever. Thank you, Rosco.

Gentle Reflections: It doesn't matter what occasion we celebrate. Each one holds very cherished memories that are everlasting. When one approaches the end of life, those occasions take on greater meaning because they will be the last. The celebration may be small and intimate or filled with a flurry of activity with family, friends, and neighbors. Let your loved one be your guide in planning such everlasting memories.

A Heavenly Birthday

It doesn't matter what the celebration. No one wants their loved one to die on special occasions or holidays customarily filled with gladness and cheer! However, the following story told by Henri Muzyka puts a whole new perspective on that thought process and a whole new meaning to *celebrate*!

I had an occasion to visit a vice-president of Sun Trust Bank about six months ago. This individual found out I worked for hospice and said, "Oh, I remember your name. You were the nurse for the father of one of our tellers. She tells us all the time how special you made her father's death."

I could not remember the daughter, the patient, or what I said or did. I was told the daughter was so apprehensive and sad that her Dad's decline made it appear he could die on her birthday and how she felt it would always taint that day.

I made a visit the day he died to say my good-byes and give his daughter a hug. Then the daughter reported through tears, "He died on my birthday."

I said (supposedly without a moment's hesitation), "Oh, now you have two things to celebrate: your birthday and the day your dad was able to go to Heaven." This person said, "That seemed to make everything okay with the daughter and in fact, made it special."

I feel so blessed to have had the field experience of nine years and the relationships with my patients and their families. We are lucky we're able to do what we do. What I have received from my patients and their families is immeasurable!

<u>Gentle Reflections</u>: These last words of Henri's are reverberated throughout hospice staff from volunteers to the administrators. Making a difference and easing the sorrow involved in the dying process are the goals of all hospice staff and volunteers.

A Living Memorial

A Thanksgiving memorial service was his last wish! My now-deceased patient wanted a memorial service where he could be physically present so he could hear what others would say about him after he died. It was a grand time! Family and friends came from every corner of the state to celebrate his living, before his dying.

After his death, his family told stories and laughed in celebration of this man's wonderful life as they surrounded him at his bedside. The tears flowed with joy and sorrow during his Life Review. What a tribute to a wonderful family-filled man...and what a grand idea!   *Judy*

On the Front Porch

Many special memories have been made on front porches around the world. The following story is about a very loved man who chose his own front porch for his last moments on earth. What an honor to share this story written by Daniel P. Klebes, Jr. Dan has spent countless hours entertaining and caring for the aged but also feels he has received countless blessings in return.

My story is one of a very personal encounter with the death of my father-in-law. Has there ever been a more joked about or maligned group as in-laws? Well, my in-laws were and continue to be a blessing to me. I don't know if I have ever met a more generous man than my late father-in-law. After working many years at the Alcoa plant in Massena, New York (quite often working 60 hours a week), "Louie" retired to tend his beloved garden in the very short summers of northern New York (summer is officially celebrated on July 10th), and to spend the eternal winters helping me keep my sanity. He was always there to encourage me and to tell me in numerous ways (often tacit) that he loved me.

Louie was so proud of his garden and he would often call to me across the yard (I lived next door) or on the phone to come and see something that was blooming. Being the quintessential "city boy" I didn't know the difference between a weed and a radish but it was always fun to share his enthusiasm, to say nothing of the best vegetables I have ever eaten.

It was early on the morning of Memorial Day 1987 that I received a phone call from my father-in-law and as usual he asked me to come up right away (his usual request) to see something. With a feigned groan I got out of bed and went directly to the garden, expecting to see my father-in-law. I was surprised to not find him there. I went into his home and my mother-in-law told me that he was in the bathroom. After a few moments he called my name and asked me to come into the bathroom. As I entered, I just knew there was something wrong and sure enough it was evident by the copious amount of blood in the toilet that something indeed was very wrong. The diagnosis was later discovered to be cancer and the prognosis was not good.

Over the next fifteen months, I spent four evenings a week sleeping on an air mattress next to his bed in his living room. Many, many things happened during this incredible sojourn which have made me a better person. During his battle, my father-in-law suffered a stroke which left him paralyzed and unable to speak, but still he was able to maintain his dignity and, even more so, a marvelous sense of humor. He especially enjoyed going for rides, and even though it was somewhat of a struggle to get him in and out of his car, it was well worth the effort.

In late August of 1988 my wife, our two children, and I went on a weeklong vacation. Immediately upon returning home we visited Louie (even before pulling into our driveway) and the grin on his face was glowing. I asked him if he missed me and his grin grew into a smile. I then asked him if he was ready to go for a ride and he responded with, "Oh boy, oh boy, oh boy!" This was one of the very few phrases he was able to speak.

Without any further adieu, we got in his car. About two minutes into the ride, I felt his good arm on my elbow and as I looked at him he was struggling to breathe. I immediately turned the car around and told my wife that as soon as we got home to call the local fire and rescue unit. Upon stopping the car, I ran to the passenger side and lifted my father-in-law up out of the car. As we approached the front door, I felt his head slump into my chest and he shared his death with me on the same front porch where he had taught me so many lessons about being a man. I love you, Louie. Thank you for being my father-in-law.

<u>Gentle Reflections</u>: The sacrifices made by family, friends, neighbors and loved ones are an expression of extreme love and concern for those who are dying. Those sacrifices of love are often made without thought of lost wages, distances to travel, families left behind to cope, or a concept of time. Unfortunately, not all patients have such support and love. For those who do, how so very thankful the dying are even if unable to say so.

The Best Of Friends

Those who are so very fortunate to have a best friend will relate to the sadness and gladness that Marjorie Welty felt as she watched her friend approaching her death. A death of a friend changes us forever. The love of a friend and the memories made with them are very precious as Marjorie tells it best.

I don't know particularly where to begin my story. Remembering makes me both sad and happy. This is a story of two very special people who came into my life when I moved to Florida. These are not their real names because Sue's husband has, after many years, remarried and started a new life, a new beginning.
Sue married young to a very abusive man. She had a son and lived in constant fear of her then husband. He was a violent man and was verbally and physically abusive. She finally left the state with her young son, boarded with a fine family, started a new job and began to live a more normal life. Some time later she met Jim. They dated for quite a while. She

hesitated to get married again but eventually did so, and Jim raised her son as his own.

They were so very happy. They settled in New Smyrna Beach, bought a lovely home and life was wonderful for them. Their happiness continued and Sue was fast approaching 50 when she discovered a lump in her breast. They saw the many doctors together and a series of tests began. One afternoon, the two of them came to our house and announced they had just left Daytona after a long consultation with several cancer specialists. The news was not good because the cancer had spread and immediate chemotherapy was to begin.

I attended some of these sessions with Sue because Jim was working and had already lost a lot of time. She was utterly fantastic! She was always in good spirits and dearly loved those people at the hospital who were trying to help her. We would go to the beach some afternoons and she would laugh and enjoy all the sights and the people. We had many long and personal talks and I would come home and be so uplifted. Can you believe she made me happy? She brought so much into my life. Some evenings my husband and I would get together with Sue and Jim and play cards. She would take off her wig and we would tease her and tell her she was probably going to be a red head when her hair came back.

During this time she also worked part-time in a local office. When she became confined to a wheelchair, she continued to work. She said she was happy to be around people, and she always had a story at night to laugh about and share with her husband.

Unfortunately the time came when Sue was confined to bed. Jim's mother came to stay with them to help. She was a very kind person and loved Sue dearly. It was a Saturday afternoon and I had decided *to spend it with Sue. When I was preparing to leave and had started to let myself out, she called for me to come back. I had already kissed her good-bye, and as I stood beside the bed, she took my hand and said, "I love you Margie." I had a heavy heart leaving that day, and an even heavier one the next morning when Jim called to say God had taken her home during the night. Sue wanted her ashes scattered over the ocean. Jim and I did that together.*

If you wonder how I felt that day, it was sadness for me, but joy for her. I knew she had already arrived at a better place and she was happy and healthy. She was quite a gal and brought a lot of happiness to those who knew her. Until hopefully we meet again Sue, you left this gal with a full heart and wonderful memories of an extremely special lady.

After Sue died, Jim volunteered for hospice for several years in appreciation for all the care Sue received the last four to six weeks before her death.

Gentle Reflections: A bond is formed that is eternal between a dying loved one, her care giving friends, and family. The sharing of intimate moments and last words and wishes form a circle of communion that can never be broken. What a privilege and honor to have a friend like Marjorie. It is true that best friends are an essential part of our well being, even in death.

A Gentle Ending

A gentle ending is what we all wish and pray for when our end-of-life approaches. Big Dan, who is from what Tom Brokaw calls the "Greatest Generation," experiences a gentle ending, as authored below in the words of his best friend, his son, Daniel P. Klebes, Jr.

Big Dan, how I love my dad… Big Dan, all 5'8" of him! As I start writing these words, I find myself laughing and crying almost at the same time, such was the relationship we shared. My dad was the second oldest of eleven children and like so many of those who lived through the depression, learned to take care of his possessions. To this day I still polish my shoes regularly, hang up my clothes promptly and squeeze every bit of toothpaste out of the tube. Don't get me wrong. My dad was very, very generous, but he did expect (that's putting it mildly) his family to respect and take care of their things. An example of his lasting impression upon his only son (me) is that I had the funeral director take Dad's shoes off and allow me to take them home and polish them before the wake. As I sat there polishing my father's shoes, I know that he was pleased.

Dad, much like my father-in-law, fought a courageous battle with cancer. He handled the entire illness with much more serenity than I could have imagined. I tried to make the 900 mile plus round trip to see my dad twice a month and each time he would tell me not to do it, that a phone call was just as good. He would say that I had a wife and family to worry about and that coming home for just one day was too much. But still I persisted and would do it all over again. My dad was physically strong as a young man, so seeing him waste away was very difficult on his family. Even though I was in my mid-forties when my dad died, I was not really prepared for the hurt his death brought me. Maybe it's because we did not always see "eye-to-eye" and did not know how to resolve certain issues, or maybe I just didn't want him to go. No matter what our differences may have been, I could always trust him when he would tell me "everything was going to be all right." Even in his death he made me know that "everything was going to be all right."

On the day he died, he was struggling to breathe and as we got him to the hospital we were all very frightened. After an hour or so he seemed to be comfortable and he suggested that we (my mother, my wife, my son, my three sisters, their husbands and children, and myself) should go home and have a good meal and come back later that evening to see him.

Before leaving, I told the rest of the family that I just wanted to spend a few moments alone with my dad. The conversation was easy and he told me that I was his whole life. Dad told me he loved me and, through tears, I told him how much I loved him and how sorry I was for ever having disappointed him. He assured me that he was very proud of me and again said that I needed to be with the family. I bent down hugged and kissed my dad and told him that I would see him later. He just smiled. Right before I left his room, he called my name and said to me, "Tell your mother I'll see her on the other side." I said, "Okay, Dad." By the time I got to my parent's home about fifteen minutes away, the hospital had called. Dad had died peacefully in his sleep. Dad was one month shy of his 68th birthday. That was ten years ago and I still miss him every day. I love you, Dad. Thank you for being my father!

Gentle Reflections: After the death of a loved one, family members often will choose family heirlooms, pictures, music or mementos to share with others in memorial services or funerals. Often each of these items will have a powerful emotion or extreme pride connected to them. What a grand way to share the life of one so loved!

In The Underwear Drawer

The author of the following story is unknown, as it has been circulated through many computer e-mails. If you know the author's name, please forward it as we wish to give credit for something so moving and profound.

A friend of mine opened his wife's underwear drawer and picked up a silk paper wrapped package. He unwrapped the box and stared at both the silk paper and the box. "She got this the first time we went to New York, eight or nine years ago. She has never put it on. She was saving it for a special occasion. Well, I guess this is it." He got near the bed and placed the gift box next to the other clothes he was taking to the funeral home, for his wife had just died. He turned to me and said, "Never save something for a special occasion. Every day in your life is a special occasion."

I still think those words changed my life. Now I read more and clean less. I sit on the porch without worrying about anything. I spend more time with my family and less at work. I understand that life should be a source of experience to be lived up to, not survived through. I no longer keep anything. I use crystal glasses every day. I wear new clothes to go to the supermarket, if I feel like it. I don't save my special perfume for special occasions. I use it whenever I want to. The words "someday…" and "one day…" are fading away from my dictionary. If it's worth seeing, listening or doing, I want to see, listen or do it now. I don't know what my friend's wife would have done if she knew she wouldn't be there the next morning, this nobody can tell. I think she might have called her relatives and closest friends. She might call old friends to make peace over past quarrels. I'd like to think she would go out for Chinese food, her favorite. It's these small things that I would regret not doing, if I knew my time had come.

I would regret it because I would no longer see the friends I would meet, write letters that I wanted to write "One of these days." I would regret and feel sad because I didn't say to my brothers and sons, not enough times at least, how much I love them. Now, I try not to delay, postpone or keep anything that could bring laughter and joy into our lives. And, on each morning, I say to myself that this could be a special day. Each day, each hour, each minute, is special.

Can You Hold Me?

During one of my hospice visits, I discovered that what we think is obvious, isn't! That's what Lucy taught me, Judy.

"Can you hold me?" The words were barely audible. I had never been asked that by a near-stranger before, so I asked Lucy, my patient, to please repeat what she said just in case I misunderstood her. The words again were just barely audible, "Can you hold me?" Then Lucy tried to lean forward in her bed

for me to gently reach around her frail body, a body that would soon be held by one much greater than I.

I wrapped my arms around Lucy's shoulders very gently so I did not hurt her or hinder her already very labored breathing. Her body felt like a wounded little bird whose love for flying had vanished. What I desired to do was to pick Lucy up and place her in the arms of the one waiting for her, but sometimes He asks for a little more patience from us. As I held Lucy, I silently prayed for her to sleep in peace and to be free from the pain that had so fiercely dwelt inside her for so long.

Next my thoughts turned to Lucy's family and the hundreds of others who attend to their dying loved ones hour after hour, day after day, and month after month. Their strength amazes me and when they say to me, "I don't know how you can do your job!" I explain to them that what they are doing is a much greater sacrifice and done with a love stronger than any other. They are the ones who deserve the praise, as there is no greater marathon in life than attending to a dying loved one.

Gentle Reflections: What Lucy taught me and the memories we made will go with me on every hospice visit I make. I will slow down and take the time to listen to and honor my patients' innocent requests, if possible, even though the request is a little out of the norm. I only had one chance to respond to what Lucy really needed as she died early the next morning.

I Shall Not Be Moved

Dr. Maya Angelou has shown us through her skill in writing poetry, screenplays, and documentaries that words can soothe a heartache that sorrow has invaded. By keeping our loved ones close in our thoughts and forever recalling precious memories, we are sweetly reminded again of the impact of their existence on our lives.

And when great souls die,
after a period peace blooms,
slowly and always
irregularly. Spaces fill
with a kind of
soothing electric vibration.
Our senses, restored, never
to be the same, whisper to us.
They existed. They existed.
We can be. Be and be
better. For they existed.

by Dr. Maya Angelou

Chapter Two

Visions and Phenomenal Senses

Beautiful visions described by the dying to their families and care providers and unusual events at the bedsides of loved ones bring a very spiritual quality to the act of dying. Events such as a mist or a scent that cannot be explained and lights surrounding survivors at an accident scene will be portrayed. While we may not understand these events sometimes they can bring comfort and peace to the patient and caregivers.

I Was Not Alone

I was on a case for Continuous Care Nursing a few years ago and we did not have a nurse for the 12am–8am shift. When I arrived, I overheard the caregiver apologizing to her aunt for falling asleep during the night and leaving her alone. Her aunt replied as she pointed to an empty chair in the corner, "I was not alone. That nice lady with the silver hair was here all night!"

Linda

See All the Little Children

Throughout their entire lives most mothers are teaching their children how to be more assertive and self-confident, while still remembering the needs of others. This story from Evelyn Mangham conveys the traits her mother instilled in her, as well as Evelyn's need to convey her own wishes instead of relying on her mom.

My mother was a gentle angel named Lola Mae Breaden. She served with her husband, George Breaden, for forty-four years as missionaries in the Middle East. They spent their last days in our home in Nyack, New York.

As my mother was nearing death, she evidently saw Heaven open! In her weak excitement, she exclaimed, "Oh, do you see all the little children? Do you see the flowers? It is all so beautiful! Can you see it?"

"Oh, Mother. Tell Jesus I love Him!" I said.

Suddenly my mother's eyes turned to me and she said, "Well, tell Him yourself!"

Ordinary Grace

Is it by chance that certain people are chosen, perhaps by fate, to be someone's caregiver or spiritual advisor as they approach death? If we consider care giving as a final gift it becomes a form of grace, kindness and an expression of love for others. The following words from Kathleen A. Brehony's book,

Ordinary Grace, are a very powerful reminder that the act of human kindness may be our greatest gift toward one another.

"We are instructed always to assume that the person sitting next to you is the Messiah waiting for some simple human kindness. It is what Mother Teresa meant when she described her work with the sick and dying people of Calcutta as 'caring for my beloved Christ in his most distressing disguises.' It is what the Dalai Lama expresses when he says, 'My religion is simple- my religion is kindness.' The Hindu salutation namaste sums it all up- it means 'the god in me recognizes the god in you.' Remember that ordinary grace requires opening ourselves up as much to the suffering of others as to their happiness. In this humble act, we recognize our unity. We find joy inside our sorrow."

Kathleen A. Brehony also emphasizes that our kindness and grace should be given without prejudice toward others as reflected in her book: "... the world's great formal religions- Hinduism, Buddhism, Judaism, Islam, and Christianity – can be likened to fingers on a hand. If we look at the fingers themselves, we see only that they are very separate. But if we follow them down to their roots, we can understand that they all come from the same hand."

It's So Beautiful!

Susan Woodard and I, Judy, had worked together in the operating room for nine years and I knew how deeply she loved her mother. I also knew the sorrow Susan felt as she watched her mother fight valiantly against numerous types of cancer which had plagued her for over thirty years. Susan shares her short but uplifting story.

Sadly, the last few days before death, my mother became unresponsive to her family and friends. When those present asked each other if she had spoken, my mother spoke instead saying, "I'm so happy! It's so beautiful!"

Gentle Reflections: When the dying experience visions of deceased family and friends, of angels, or a deity such as Jesus, there can be no greater comfort to them or their loved ones. These visions may be seen days or weeks prior to death. Their hands may outstretch to touch those they see or they may visit with them as they would you. Ask your loved one to describe their visions and those they see. Your loved one may even get overly excited and want to get dressed and pack a bag for their final earthly trip. There is no fear experienced in these events but rather a spiritual comfort and joy felt by the dying and their loved ones. What an everlasting gift!

The Carpenter in the Garden

Sue Mossman shares another story that yields a look inside of Heaven through a carpenter and gardener's eyes.

You tell me. How can a patient on a strong pain-killer speak so clearly the thoughts going through his mind? My patient was a fifty year-old man who had returned to his family for his last few weeks when Continuous Care nurses had been called in.

His mom was sitting at the bedside holding his hand and telling of his work as a "finish" carpenter. He constructed beautiful moldings and trim work and had worked primarily in the "high-end" construction of home building. The only regret he had was that he didn't have room for a flower garden since he lived in Brooklyn, and only had room for a window box on his fire escape. He missed having a lot of flowers around.

Even though we had not heard a word from our patient in days, on this particular evening as his mom was gently stroking his forehead he said, "Ma, you should see the woodwork in this place! There are acres and acres of flowers!"

After my patient died, I saw his mom in the grocery store several times and she told me she still smiles and feels such comfort when she thinks of his remarks. She knows he is happy surrounded by his beautiful woodwork and acres and acres of flowers.

In Loving Memory of My Dad
Edward C. Sparks
November 9, 1913--March 22, 2003

A daughter, Donna Berrong, lovingly tells how the comfort found in a bluebird, white horses, and the love of a family can ease one's passing to a much grander place.

On July 3, 1937, Edward "Ted" Sparks and Elsie Silcox were married. Back then neither Ted nor Elsie knew that they had to make arrangements to get married. They had gone to the local courthouse and got their marriage license. On the way back they saw the preacher coming down the road and flagged him down. The preacher married them right there on the side of the road! Years later, the spot where they were married was turned into a junkyard.

As the years came and went, us kids, my brothers, Ed, Fred, Pat and I, told everyone that Mom and Dad were married in a junkyard, but their marriage lasted 65 years until the death of my dad. If he had lived until July 3, 2003, it would have been 66 years. Maybe everyone should be married in a junkyard if marriages would last 65 years.

My dad was ill for several months but we were lucky enough to have him three months longer than the doctors thought he would live. During the time before he died, especially the last month, my dad talked to his sisters, brothers, and a niece who had passed. But one night around 2:00 am, Dad woke me up and said, "Dump, (the nickname he had always called me) call the bluebird."

I said, "I don't know how to call the bluebirds." If my dad used the word "duh" he would have said "Duh, just say bluebird."

Well, I called the bluebird but it would not come to me. So I told my dad, "Daddy, the bluebird will not come to me. Since you have a way with animals, why don't you call it?"

My dad said, "bluebird," then he stuck out his finger and he started petting the bluebird that had landed on his finger. My dad saw a bluebird as if it were real. I have no doubt about it after seeing his reaction.

My dad also saw four white horses, twice. The first time was just before hospice first came. Again it was around 2:00 am and he was trying to get out of bed to go to the horses. I asked him what he was trying to do and he said that he was trying to get to the horses. I asked him how many there were and he told me four white horses. I told him that his legs were too weak and for him to call the horses to him. He called the horses then he reached out in the midair and petted them.

I had the honor of helping my dad go to a better place. I talked to him before he died and told him that he would be able to do all the things that he hadn't been able to do for years. I talked to him for about an hour and forty-five minutes before he passed. I told him to get on the biggest, whitest horse. Her name was "Dump" and she would take him to Heaven. After I said those words, my dad smiled and took his last breath. I have no doubt that he went to a better place at that moment because he died so peacefully and had a beautiful smile on his face.

God bless the people of hospice for helping us. Without them, I'm not sure how we could have made it through such a trying and tiring time. My dad was everything to each of us and we miss him dearly but we would not want him back the way he was before his death. The hospice staff helped him live his last week with dignity and without pain. My dad felt they could do no wrong and my family would have to agree.

I See Jesus

It is a very moving and blessed event for one to share an experience as nurse C.J. Baigas did, especially when her patient sees Jesus.

I was called at home one day about noon by a Primary Care Nurse to ask me to take a specific Continuous Care case. This was very unusual because I am normally contacted by a scheduling person but in this instance a fellow nurse asked me if I could go to this particular home now. I told her I was busy and couldn't go at 4 pm, the usual time for the second shift to start.

The nurse said, "I really need you to go now. This patient is a 62-year-old woman with pancreatic cancer. She is having no pain, and on no medications but it is a very difficult family situation. Her 84 year-old mother is there at her daughter's home and she is so into her own grief that she is keeping Mary Ann's husband and children away from the bedside. Death is getting close. I need a mediator. Will you go?"

I said I would and hurriedly got into my uniform. I truly believe the Lord sends me where I am meant to go and that I would miss some wonderful experiences if I said no.

I arrived just before 1 pm and was introduced to the family by the primary nurse. The family members were all distraught: Mary Ann's husband John, their three grown daughters, and of course, Mary Ann's mother Jane. Mary Ann was an only child and Jane kept repeating, "No one should have to go through the pain of losing their only child. It should be me instead."

I comforted her as best I could and asked her if I could have a moment with Mary Ann to do an assessment, although I could see that Mary Ann was going to go to Heaven today. Jane stepped out and joined John and the children, who were in the living room. I could feel the tension.

I talked gently to Mary Ann while I did vital signs and a quick assessment. Her blood pressure was 90/60 and her heart rate was 124. She did not open her eyes while I talked to her but I could sense that she understood what I was saying. I told her I could see she was not in physical pain, and that I could only imagine her emotional pain with what was happening with the family. I assured her that I would do what I could to help.

Over the next couple of hours, I tended to Mary Ann and her family. I learned they were Christians, and all knew Mary Ann was "going to Heaven very soon."

I asked Jane to come out and tell me about Mary Ann, thus allowing her husband and children some private time with her. Jane told me about Mary Ann growing up and shared recollections from her life, while John and the children each spent private time with Mary Ann.

I went back into the bedroom and I could see changes happening fairly quickly. I had rubbed Mary Ann's back, moistened her mouth and repositioned her in bed as needed. She showed no signs of pain or anxiety. She had not opened her eyes nor spoken since my arrival. I gave a quiet report to the family of the changes. The environment was more peaceful and the family, especially Jane, seemed more resigned to the fact that Mary Ann would not be with them much longer.

I continued to try to see that all the family members had time at the bedside. Jane was not able to give her daughter permission to leave when she was ready, although the rest of the family did so. Jane continued to lament the approaching loss of her daughter, and I comforted her as best I could.

I had been in Mary Ann's home about five hours when I felt she was getting very close to her moment of death. I took her blood pressure again. I could barely hear it, I called the family to the bedside and I said to her, "Mary Ann, pretty soon you are going to see a white light. Just go toward it when you are ready."

She opened her eyes, looked straight at me and said, "I see the light." I was truly shocked because I hadn't expected any response.

I then said to her, "Mary Ann, when you are ready, go through the light and you will see Jesus."

She got a beautiful peaceful look on her face, opened her eyes again, looked straight at me and said, "I see Jesus, and He is so beautiful." Her eyes closed, her breathing got very shallow, slowed and stopped.

We were all stunned. I have never before nor since had a patient talk to me with a blood pressure so low. The family was all comforted but none more than Jane. We discussed this astounding event, all deeply touched, and I shared with Jane that I felt the Lord had allowed this event so Jane could better deal with the pain of her loss. She was much comforted by this final earthly gift from her beloved daughter. I heard no further cries unto God as to how He could let this happen.

We gently bathed and dressed Mary Ann in the clothes her daughters picked out. After the funeral home driver had come and gone, we all exchanged hugs and good-byes. As I drove away, I thought how close I had come to missing this truly breathtaking experience, and I again marveled at God's love, compassion and mercy, with a miracle thrown in for us all.

Veronica's Image

Won't it be nice to find that perfect job once we get to where we're going after death? Helen Disch's patient did!

What an artist! She loved and made beautiful things. Now she was sick and had moved in with her daughter and son-in-law who loved her very much. A special pump, that would automatically deliver pain medication, was attached to her. Each evening after 5:00 pm, all her family of fifteen to twenty would come to visit.

One night her granddaughter decorated her hair with a garland of flowers and she had a long-stem rose as a scepter. All of her family gathered around the bed. She waved her flower at each one, stating what they were to get in the will. Then she asked, "Did I recognize everyone?" I showed her a picture of Jesus and asked her if she recognized him.

She said, "He was here yesterday and stood on this side (indicating her right side) about three feet away. The man did not speak but I got a warm feeling from him. He hasn't been back since."

I told her, "Maybe he is looking for someone to be in charge of his art department."

"Oh, that would be wonderful. I could do that!" she replied. She left for her new job a few weeks later.

I Saw Angels

Joseph's eyes were wide open! His eyes were slowly following something moving around his bed from the left side to the right. He had no fear in his face and didn't respond when I asked him what he saw.

It didn't take long to figure out what it may have been that Joseph was seeing. His mother Maggie explained, "Judy, there were three angels all dressed in white. I didn't see any wings but I know there were angels around my son's bed. I was watching them from across the room. I couldn't see their faces as their backs were to me. There was such a beautiful glow around them! No one believes me, but I know I saw them and I've seen them before today!"

Gentle Reflections: As I, Judy, sit and watch my patients like Joseph, I try to imagine what they must be seeing and feeling. As I watch my patient's hands reach for or watch someone at their bedside, that I can't envision, I feel blessed to witness such a spiritual moment. It is a joy of reassurance and comfort for the dying, and for myself, to know that there must be another spiritual existence that we are going to once we leave this earth.

Dave's Angels

Judy Richotte takes you by the hand and leads you through around-the-clock nursing care at a patient's bedside, which is a great support and comfort not only for patients but also for their families and loved ones. Judy and her co-workers lovingly and loyally provide care to their hospice patient as you will see in this story.

Dave was approximately seventy years old. He had big, beautiful, blue eyes and a smile that lit up a room. I spent nearly three weeks with him while he approached death and needed assistance in controlling his symptoms. My co-workers, JoAnne Parrish and Tommie Griffin, and myself shared Dave's around-the-clock care. We had quickly formed a special bond with Dave and his wife Nancy.

After the first couple of days, Dave was bed-bound and so consented to a hospital bed being placed in the master bedroom next to the bed he and Nancy had shared for many years. Dave would watch television, pretend to read the newspaper (he was too restless to concentrate, even with medication) and we would talk for hours. We had our daily ritual. After breakfast Dave used the bedside commode, had a bed bath, took naps, and even had a pedicure and manicure, which he loved!

When Dave could no longer smoke his cigarettes, he wore a nicotine patch and did well with the patch and other medications, such as Haldol and Ativan.

As his time came closer, Dave became more anxious. One day Dave admitted to me that he was sorry he wouldn't be going to Heaven, as he hadn't been to church in twenty years or more. I assured Dave that God loved him and though he wasn't a churchgoer he was a good loving husband and father (he had two sons, both police officers in south Florida plus four grandchildren) and was a good friend and neighbor to many. I called the hospice chaplain, Mark Rath, and Mark came to see Dave that very day. Dave and Mark were alone in the bedroom for an hour or more. After Mark left, I entered the bedroom and Dave said, "Guess what? You're right! Mark said I'll get into Heaven. I'm so happy and relieved." Dave, Nancy and I hugged and said a prayer to thank God for the wonderful feelings of peace Dave was experiencing.

Dave was, however, having increased restlessness, which hospice calls "terminal restlessness." The last day he was at home, Nancy and I took turns during most of the day lying in the hospital bed next to Dave, trying to keep him in bed and quiet. By 5 pm, after consultation with the Continuous Care supervisor Fran Davis and Dave's doctor, we were on our way to the hospital emergency room. Dave had not closed his eyes in three days, was unable to sleep or relax, and no amount or kind of medication was working for him.

Dave was admitted to the oncology floor that night. Dave's doctor ordered Continuous Care to continue in the hospital at the patient and family's request. Nancy and their sons, Mike and Larry, took turns resting in the next bed, as JoAnne, Tommie and I carried on as caregivers and were now known as "Dave's Angels," per Dave and Nancy. We each wore the same little pewter angel on our uniform every day.

One day, Dave whispered to me, "There are two angels in the corner. One is really big with huge wings.

He's the one that will fly me to heaven. Please tell them I'm not ready yet. Give me a couple of days."

I walked over to the corner and spoke to the angels, relaying Dave's request.

"They're gone now but they'll be back." Dave said.

That day the doctor started a morphine drip after conferring with Nancy and their family. They all said their good-byes, as did I, as Dave's sleep would come quickly and there would be no real conversation in the few days left. As Dave became increasingly drowsy, he kept moving his hand to his mouth clumsily. I realized Dave was trying to smoke an imaginary cigarette. I put my finger in his mouth and he sucked weakly on it and blew as if puffing on a cigarette. I did this for several minutes and he occasionally smiled at me. In his eyes I saw, "Thank you, friend/nurse!"

The day Dave was last conscious, just before sleep overtook him, his last words were, "I love you." He looked in the corner of the room and said, "They're back for me, I'll be going with them soon."

Dave died peacefully in the hospital a couple of days later with myself, Nancy and Larry at his bedside. How I'll miss those beautiful eyes and that smile!

Momma

Gail Hageman witnessed the beauty of her hospice patient's smile when, prior to his death, he envisioned his mother who had died years prior

On Tuesday Joseph was transferred to a nursing home and was unhappy that his wife could no

longer care for him at home. He was sick, he was tired and he didn't want to talk to me.
I went with him to the nursing home and sat at his bedside. He didn't open his eyes and he didn't speak. He just laid there. Suddenly he sat bolt upright in the bed with the most glorious smile on his face as he reached out his hand to the foot of the bed and stated, "Momma! I've missed you so much!"
I observed a teary, animated Joseph talking with someone I could not see. After a few short minutes, he said his good-byes and lay back in the bed. A small smile played on his face. I said my good-byes and went home. I called his wife that evening and asked if he called her Momma? "Oh, no" she said, "that is what he called his mother and she has been dead for years." I recalled the story of what I had seen. Joseph died that night.

You're Blocking Their View

Judy's patient Wally, age 78, lay in a light coma but he was still able to respond through the squeeze of his hand and with a sweet grin on his lips. No words ever left his lips in the eight hours Judy sat at his bedside during his last day alive. Somehow, Wally still communicated to those around him.

As Wally's three adult children circulated through his bedroom, I learned many wonderful things about Wally. He was a widower and sorely missed his loving spouse, even after a dozen years. He and his wife had also shared a tragedy in the loss of an infant daughter many years prior.

Wally's eldest son shared an experience with me that had occurred the day prior. He had just stepped into his father's bedroom and as he stood in the doorway his father said, "Son, you need to move. You're standing in her way!"

He asked his father, "Whose way am I standing in?"

Wally answered, "Your mother's, of course!"

Later in the same day, Wally's son had sat next to his father's bed in front of the closet door. Wally said, "Son, you need to move. You are blocking your mother and sister!" The only sister that could have possibly been spoken of was the infant who died many years prior.

What a comfort those two experiences were for the family to know that their mother and sister were waiting patiently to take their dad with them!

Ethel's Back!

Lawrence's wife Ethel had died seven months prior to Judy's visit with Lawrence and his family. They all spoke so highly of her and missed her dearly. Unfortunately, shortly after Ethel's death, Lawrence noticed some difficulty breathing, especially with any exertion or exercise. Plus, he had a nagging cough. So off to the doctor Lawrence went, only to find out that he had lung cancer, which was far beyond any successful chance of treatment.

During my visit, I sat together with the family in the sun-filled living room where we discussed what laid ahead for their Dad and them. As we talked, the family shared stories of their dad regarding recent events involving their mother.

For example: One day Lawrence was sitting in the recliner with his feet up when he jumped as if startled by something. Lawrence said, "Ethel, be more careful now! You just brushed against my feet! " Yup, you guessed it! Ethel was teasing Lawrence and silently reminding him she was patiently waiting for him. Lawrence was sure of that!

Three Visions

This story is about a man who saw his deceased wife three times prior to his own passing. The storyteller is Kate Ryan, a hospice nurse.

Norman passed away in the fall of 1998. His stepdaughters said that their stepfather was ready because he had seen his wife three times in recent weeks. Norman's wife had passed away two years prior.

The first time that Norman saw his wife was when he was last in the hospital. In his mind, he came back to his house and Mama was there, but she would not talk to him.

The second time he saw his wife was less than two weeks prior to his death when he was at home in bed. She appeared to him and said, "Everything will be okay."

The third time she appeared to him was the week of his death and she said, "Get your clothes on and come with me." Norman then tried to get out of bed and get dressed.

<u>Gentle Reflections</u>: As the dying person nears death, they may see and even converse with deceased family members or spiritual figures we cannot see. They may express pure joy and a sense of peace in reaction to seeing a beautiful place. This phenomenon is known in the hospice community as nearing death awareness and it appears to bring serenity and peace to the dying individual and their loved ones.

Mary's Spirit

Elsie Hudome spent the final minutes with her patient Mary who gave her a very rare look at what may have been her patient's spirit exiting her body.

I had been pondering the events surrounding death. Having had so many varied experiences while working with hospice, I was thinking about the aspect of physical death and what happens at the moment of death. I believe we have a soul that departs for another place. As a nurse, I had always been more involved in the physical part and really wished for some insight on the spiritual aspect.

My beeper went off and I received a Continuous Care case with an elderly woman who was imminently dying. When I arrived at the home, the niece who had been her caregiver met me at the door with, "Thank goodness you're here. I love Mary very much but I can't watch this anymore."

Mary was in a small room lying quietly and peacefully in a single bed. The room was a little sparse compared to the rest of the house as if it was quickly made into a bedroom. I assessed Mary and found her to be declining rapidly, which I conveyed to the family. More family members had arrived and were conversing in the dining room.

I sat with Mary holding her hand so that she knew she was not alone. Family members would sift in and out of the room intermittently. For most, it seems uncomfortable to talk to someone who does not seem to know you are there. The words do not come easily.

As I sat with Mary, it occurred to me that I was again going to be attending a death and the family was not keen on being present when it occurred. I soon began to think about paying very close attention in order to take in every detail. Suddenly, I felt an urge to ask Mary's permission to see her soul leave. In the next instant that seemed ludicrous. But no, maybe not. What did I have to lose? So, silently I asked her permission.

Within twenty minutes, Mary's respirations became erratic. I let the family know what was happening and they again did not wish to be present. I sat by Mary, watching, waiting, and holding her hand as her pulse became imperceptible. Then Mary opened her eyes, turned her head towards me and looked at me, really looked at me, not through me as if a blank stare. Then she turned her head back, closed her eyes and ceased to breathe. My gaze had not wavered and at that moment I saw a faint white wisp of what looked like steam/vapor waft above Mary's head and disappear. For a moment, it was impossible to move. I believe that Mary gave me permission to see the essence of her leave for her next journey.

The Halos

Linda was working the day shift for Continuous Care with Rose, a 92-year-old lady, who was very near the end of her life. Rose's daughter and Linda became a great team in caring for Rose at the end of her life.

We actually began working with such unison it was amazing. We began to spontaneously get up to do things for Rose with the same intentions, and we were aware of this. We talked a great deal about issues of spirituality and how amazing this was in itself. Rose's daughter was a very spiritual individual and had great faith and wanted nothing more for her mom but a graceful end to her life.

On the next morning, Rose's daughter and I observed something even more amazing. I was sitting on one side of the bed and Rose's daughter was sitting on the other. I observed what appeared to be smoke rings coming from Rose's mouth. Sure I was seeing things, I said nothing. Rose's daughter looked at me and said, "Oh, do you see the halos, too?"

Rose died later that evening very peaceful and with the grace her daughter wanted for her mom.

Gentle Reflections: I am not sure exactly what it was we saw. I have read of the spirit leaving the body in the form of a mist or vapor, and I have seen it many times in my work. I met a nurse's aide who was part Native American. She opened the window in the patient's room minutes before he died and explained that she believed it allowed the spirit a way to leave.

You Take the High Road

On occasion, if one wants to be introduced to a spirit, it is as simple as asking to be, as Helen Disch discovered.

Her name was Janet Macky and she was of Scottish descent. She was receiving twenty-four-hour continuous nursing care for several days before her son Ranny arrived from the New Jersey area. Janet was still able to talk to us.

One night I was talking to her about the paintings by her brother that decorated her living room and bedroom. Her brother was a minister. We talked about him another night and I asked her if he was in the room. She said he was right behind me. I was standing on my patient's right. I said, "Tell him to introduce himself." Suddenly, I got the iciest, cold tingle down my right arm. I asked her who that was and she replied, "That's my brother, John."

Later that evening while she was sleeping, her son said that he noticed a shimmering area near her bedroom door that looks like the air you see in a desert mirage or atop a distant hot road.

From that point, Janet slept most of the time. She took the high road to the bonny banks of Loch Lomond on June 24th at 11:15 pm. She loved the bagpipes and was piped out in true Scottish fashion with the "Skye Boat Song," followed by a stirring rendition of "Scotland the Brave."

<u>Gentle Reflections</u>: It has long been speculated in books and documentaries that the spirit of the dying person leaves the body in the form of a mist or vapor. I have pondered myself where the essence of the person goes when the physical body dies. What part of us makes up the soul? The part of us that makes us who we are, how we think, feel and respond to the world around us is not physical, so therefore how can it die?

Brown Eyes Turn Blue

Sometimes the unexplained is best left in the care of angels, as Helen Disch explains in this story about Henry's Eyes.

My Continuous Care patient named Henry was in a nursing home near the beach. He was very spiritual and loved his big family, which included three sets of twins. His oldest son, who was very tall and looked like an NFL player, wanted a photo of himself with his pappy. Then other family members wanted to be included. The patient's daughter read Psalms at his bedside. Henry didn't speak but did understand and listened to words about Heaven.

Towards the end of my shift, the patient was trying to raise his eyebrow in answer to questions and mouthing answers. He was waiting for one of his twins

to arrive but his family told him, "Marvin can't be here because he won't fly." They urged him to go to Heaven.
When I checked my patient's eyes, they had turned from brown to blue. His children cried out that he had seen the angels. Carol Lavargna LPN and many other staff members came in to look at Henry's new blue eyes. When the midnight nurse's aide Judy Roberson arrived, she too was surprised. What made them so different was that Henry was an African-American with very dark skin. The family said that the spirit had hit his eyes and now they were the color of the sky. Henry went to be with the angels that morning at 4:49.

Gentle Reflections: For certain, Henry's eyes changing from brown to blue defies explanation. Does there really need to be an explanation? The family's belief that the "spirit had hit his eyes" is an awesome thought and it just possibly brought them some joy and peace to ease the sorrow in their loss.

The Gathering

As a hospice nurse, it is not unusual to see families gather from other parts of the country when a family member is dying. In this story Linda explains how certain events can be shared by many from earth and Heaven.

On this particular case, my patient Liz had been a hospice patient for a long time and was coming to the end of her journey. Her adult children had all gathered at the daughter's house where Liz was staying. They had prepared a room with a partition just off the dining room where Liz could have some privacy, yet still be close to everyone and at some level enjoy the activities of the family. As they prepared a Thanksgiving-like dinner, they shared memories with each other. They would laugh a little and they would cry a little.

We were short a nurse for one shift of Continuous Care so the day nurse and I decided to split the shifts into twelve hour shifts, as it was apparent that some family members were not aware as to how close Liz was to completing her journey. The day nurse took the family members aside to prepare them for how close it really was and all agreed to a chaplain visit.

It was close to 9 pm when the chaplain arrived. Prayer was provided with everyone gathered around Liz. An amazing thing happened shortly after the prayer. When everyone stepped away to have dessert, the aroma of pipe tobacco surrounded Liz. When I asked Liz's daughter, "Who smokes the pipe?" her daughter stepped back over by Liz's bed and replied, "Dad and Uncle Bill," who were Liz's husband and brother who died a few years ago. Liz died at noon the next day.

I'm Not Afraid to Die

After Joan Green cared for her hospice patient, she described the beauty and peace revealed to her patient in her final days through visions and enhanced senses.

Mrs. Post was a 94-year-old petite lady on our hospice program. She had poor vision and was very hard of hearing. She was a teacher for many years and had many stories to tell to anyone who would listen! She married late in life and had no children. Her husband had died several years prior.

Toward the end of her care, Mrs. Post's blood pressure had dropped four mornings in a row. That concerned us, but she always rallied within thirty minutes.

One morning I received a call from the nursing home stating Mrs. Post's blood pressure had dropped to 42/28. The nurse said, "I feel she's not going to make it. I can't get a pulse."

I called Mrs. Post's nephew to update him on the changes in her condition. He stated he would come as soon as he could get away. The nursing home was notified that he would be coming and I would be there soon. The nurse said she had their Certified Nursing Assistant sitting with Mrs. Post holding her hand, and so far there was no change.

When I arrived later at the nursing home, I found Mrs. Post had rallied. She was alert and excited. She told the nursing assistant, "It was so beautiful and warm. If I knew dying was this beautiful I would have done it sooner. I don't know why God didn't keep me. I guess because I've been so quiet and he wanted me to tell everyone how beautiful it is. Now I'm not afraid to die."

When her nephew arrived, I explained to him how she changed and that we could hardly believe it. I went in to the room with him. Mrs. Post was able to hear and talk plainly. I left them alone. Later he came out and said, "I just can't believe it. She hasn't been able to hear me for several months and I couldn't understand her on recent visits. We had a good talk."

A couple of hours later, Mrs. Post asked for something to eat. She said, "I don't want to leave here without having some chocolate pudding." She ate all of it.

Her story was told to everyone who entered the room. All were amazed that they could understand her. The next few days she was out of bed in her wheelchair and propelling herself around to tell her story to anyone who would listen.

One day as she sat in her wheelchair alone in her room, the nursing assistant came by and saw Mrs. Post looking up and all around and heard her talking. As the nursing assistant entered the room, Mrs. Post said, "Don't you see them? The angels... they're all around me and are so beautiful."

Later the chaplain came to visit her. She was dressed all in white and told him, "I'm going tomorrow and I want to be ready." Mrs. Post stated she was worried about her things when she dies. She called the social worker in to make a list of her things and to whom they should go to.

Several days passed and Mrs. Post was still waiting to go. Every day she said she was ready to go. God chose to take her May 23, 2003. She left peacefully.

Gentle Reflections: Other phenomena often witnessed by caregivers are enhanced senses. This could be the sense of smell, hearing or sight. This phenomenon not only affects the dying person but also, at times, the caregivers such as with the aroma of pipe tobacco when no one present smoked a pipe. It is widely believed that loved ones of the dying who have already died come for them. Could the scent of the pipe tobacco have been a sign for this family of just that? I have heard many times of the scent of a favorite flower or perfume being present at the bedside of the dying.

The return of the sense of hearing and improved vision for Mrs. Post was truly a gift. It lifted her spirits and took away her fear of dying and made it possible to have that "good talk" with her nephew. Do these amazing events truly need explanation or should we just accept them as the gifts they are, no matter what the explanation?   Linda

How Did He Know?

Often times we can get directions from our patients if we listen and watch carefully. Howard sure taught me, Judy, a few things about love, laughter and living.

As I sat and watched melting orange Popsicle drip down my patient's hand, I thought of how witty and determined Howard was to succeed, despite his weakness, as he approached death. His wife, Joyce, and his granddaughter, Katina, had been at his bedside nearly every waking moment during his last days. They shared many beautiful memories as I attended to Howard one evening.

Katina, a very special lady who is fourteen years old, only weighed one and one-half pounds when she was born! She was in the hospital for months after her birth before she was able to go home. I know that for sure because she shared her baby pictures with me.

Katina was a very typical teenager who had a great love for her grandparents. In fact, their love is so grand that Katina and Howard had learned sign

language to tell each other, "I love you!" By the way, neither Katina or Howard were deaf. After Katina signed her love to her grandfather, Howard had barely enough strength to raise his arms to return the same signed love for his granddaughter.

An odd occurrence happened with Howard, which commonly does when you attend to the dying. Howard had spoken very few words during the hours I was with him. Out of the blue, Howard gained enough strength to say, "Let's go on vacation." Katina asked him where he would like to go. Her grandfather responded, "On the Mississippi River on a boat."

Well, I almost fell out of my chair because several days prior to attending to Howard, I had discussed vacation plans with my husband and had researched on the Internet about cruising the Mississippi River on a steamboat! I mentioned this afterwards to Joyce and she said they had never discussed such an idea and didn't know where his idea had come from. But, thanks to Howard, we have decided to ride the Mississippi River!

Gentle Reflections: Thank you Joyce and Katina for the joy I found and memories I made of Howard's drippy Popsicles, not winning at Jeopardy, winning on Wheel of Fortune, and verifying where I should go on vacation! In fact, I did get to ride on the Mississippi River on a steamboat the summer after Howard died where I saw hundreds of Canadian geese resting on the water! I wish you pleasant dreams and may all your days be filled with signs of love from Howard!

The Greatest Send-Off

Helen Disch was present the day of a thunder-clapping, lightning flashing send-off of her patient. It was a day she'll never forget!

Mary Lou was very poor. She lived in an old singlewide trailer that had seen better days. Her furniture was old and sparse. Things had not been going well for her lately. All she had was the beauty of the land and the wildlife, which she truly loved. Her only son John was in his forties and was at her bedside. John stated that he had a hard time trying to read but he wanted to be able to read the Bible someday. It had just begun to rain as he sat at her bedside holding her hand. This woman was leaving with only her son to say good-bye. There would be no big send-off as she was within five minutes of leaving.

I knew the three-fold blessing, so I stood at the end of the bed and raised my hands over her feet. At that minute, the largest lightning bolt and the loudest crack of thunder I had ever heard came on both sides of the trailer. All Heaven had come down for the send-off. Her son began to pray loudly in tongues, brought by the spirit. This all lasted approximately three minutes. I put my arms down and moved to the side of the bed. Her son said, "She just left. The spirit has gone, but everything was perfect. She has gone to

Heaven. I guess the best came for the greatest send-off."

Gentle Reflections: Mary Lou lived a humble life and took joy in the beauty of the land and wildlife. How fitting of Mother Nature's timing to orchestrate this storm for a great send-off just at the right moment.

In Memory of John Ruffin
May 14,1974--September 9, 2000

Death does not always come at the bedside, nor is it always a serene, peaceful event as in a sudden tragic death such as occurred with Linda's son-in-law.

It was September 9, 2000, my fiftieth birthday. I received a telephone call at 5 am from my daughter Tara." We are on our way, Mom." My daughter, son in law and granddaughter were coming to Florida from North Carolina to celebrate my birthday and to take our granddaughter to some of the places we had taken Tara when she was a little girl.
At 5:20 am we received another call, "Mom, John is dead!"
"What do you mean?" I asked in disbelief.
"He's dead, Mom. We were hit! I have got to go to the hospital now!" And she hung up.
My husband Dan was already up and sitting at the kitchen table, as he intuitively knew when that second call came it was not good news. We made a few phone calls, readied ourselves for the trip ahead and left shortly after for North Carolina.

It seemed like it was the longest trip we ever made. We could not talk or listen to the radio. We had to hold it together to get there safely. Our emotions were like none we had ever experienced. We were in shock and saddened by the news of John's death, and so grateful at the same time that the girls were not harmed. What comfort could we possibly provide to David and Faye, (John's parents) whose only child had been taken by death. It was a tough drive.

We arrived in North Carolina approximately nine hours later. With my daughter in my arms, she exclaimed, "I have had my butt kicked, Mom!" (Tara had the idea that she was ten feet tall and bulletproof).

Many of John's relatives had already arrived and we were told about the circumstances of the accident. The car was hit from behind while sitting at a traffic light just after John and Tara had gotten gas for the trip.

Tara told us how she tried to get John out of the car but could not get the window open. She had felt John and he was soft and warm and she thought he was alive and just unconscious.

The rescue people had arrived on the scene and she had yelled to them to help her get him out because she knew CPR. By the time she got to John, she knew it was too late. She said, "I just took him in my arms and held him and told him how much I loved him!"

The funeral was held on September 11. It was a beautiful service and they played Vince Gill's song, "Go Rest High On That Mountain." John's dad took Jesus into his life that day, as did many others. On the road to the cemetery, I noticed all the police officers that were posted to escort the procession had their hats placed over their hearts. I was deeply moved and comforted by this, as I am sure everyone else was.

When we arrived back at John's parents home, Faye told us that one of the rescue persons had come by to tell her this: "When we arrived on the scene of the accident, we saw a light around the woman and the child, like a halo type light!"

This declaration gave much comfort to all. In my heart I believe it was John's light, as I knew how much and how deeply he loved Tara and Auslynn. I believe he could not have left this world without knowing they were all right.

With heavy hearts, Dan and I knew we had to return to Florida. We bid our farewells with the promise that I would return as often and as soon as I could to just be there through the next year. On the way home, we were still unable to talk much or play the radio. When we hit the Florida state line, we decided to put the radio on and much to our surprise the song that was playing was Vince Gill's "Go Rest High On That Mountain."

As a hospice nurse, I have seen the gifts built into the dying process that comfort the ones left behind when the patient dies. I have often wondered if these gifts were provided with sudden death. I now believe they are.

About six weeks after John died, my daughter told me of an experience she had one night. She was very depressed and was begging to see John one more time. She wanted to feel him one more time, hold him one more time. She said she woke up somewhere around 3 am and she could see John standing in the doorway of her bedroom. She went to him and he held her in his arms. She said, "Mom, I could feel his warmth. I could even smell him, and I knew everything would be okay." This experience gave her more comfort then I can describe. It gave her strength to go on and it gave her peace.

To John, just like that coffee cup I gave you one Christmas says, "I know you are my son-in-law but my heart calls you son."

<u>Gentle Reflections</u>: This tragic event took place over three years ago. Today, I travel to North Carolina every April to celebrate my granddaughter's birthday and to celebrate life. We gather with John's family for a good old-fashioned North Carolina barbecue and simply enjoy being together. Our granddaughter is in school now and is a happy normal six-year-old. Our daughter Tara has obtained a degree in forestry and is actively seeking employment in her field, and she is dating.

Does an event like this change your life? Of course it does and it should. I find myself hard-pressed to get angry with anyone. Am I capable of getting angry? Sure I am. I choose to have more joy in my life over strife. I like to hug more. Unfortunately you cannot walk around hugging everyone so I give everyone a smile just to let him or her know I know you are here and you matter. Whether it is a life ending disease or sudden tragic death, death teaches us how to live if we but listen. Be aware of how precious life really is and that every life is a gift and could be gone tomorrow. Death is the great equalizer, it has no boundaries, and it is the one sure thing we all have in common. So hug more when you can and smile when you can't.   Linda

Chapter Three

The Inspiring Human Spirit

Autonomy is the ability or tendency to function independently and the right to self-direction. Most often, the physical ability for independence is lost for the dying; however, when allowed to die on one's own terms, it brings a sense of independence and dignity to the one facing the end of life. Families of the dying also gain from having some control over these very difficult times. The strength of the human spirit is clear in the following stories from the grace displayed by a husband as his wife's life slips away, to Sam and others who show an amazing will to have self-direction in their dying, even orchestrating their time of death.

Hearts

As a hospice nurse, it is common for our patients and families to tug at our hearts. I will never forget the husband of one of my very first patients. When I arrived at this home, the patient was actively dying. What moved me was the patient's husband. As he softly wept, he held his hand over his wife's heart until it stopped. I cannot think of a more graceful good-bye   Linda

Uncle Mel

C.J. Baigas is again blessed as she witnesses final gifts like Uncle Mel's.

I was asked to take a case in DeLeon Springs, Florida, with Mel, a 76 year-old man with end-stage respiratory disease. He lived with his niece, Sharon, and her husband Jeff. Continuous Care Nursing was to begin with my shift from 8 am-4 pm.

I arrived and was greeted by Sharon who shared that she had essentially been raised by Mel who had never married, and he had been a father to her. They were very close. After introducing himself, Jeff left for work with instructions for us to call if Mel's condition changed.

Mel was essentially unresponsive to my assessment. He had received very good care from Sharon and Jeff and I was told he had been able to talk a little bit to them the day before, but had not been able to respond since about 9 pm the previous evening.

Sharon and I spoke outside the room and I shared with her what I was seeing regarding disease progression and the dying process. Mel was on several medications and oxygen to ease his breathing, and he was very peaceful. Mel's primary nurse had done a wonderful job of education as Mel's disease progressed, so there wasn't much Sharon didn't already realize.

Sharon and I sat in Mel's bedroom and she quietly began to tell me about "Uncle Mel." He had always been a bachelor but gladly took over the task of raising her when both her parents were killed in an auto accident when she was fourteen. She reminisced about being a teenager with a "bachelor father" and recalled some of the wonderful times they had shared. She told me Uncle Mel had always used his wonderful smile when other disciplines weren't working, and that she "would miss that beautiful smile more than words can say." At this time, Sharon was 8 months pregnant with her first child. "It's a boy, and we are going to name him Mel. I just wish Uncle Mel could still be here when he's born," Sharon said.

We held hands and talked about guardian angels, God, and "Uncle Mel". She felt that Uncle Mel would be his "grandson's" guardian angel, and that gave her comfort. I reinforced with her that Uncle Mel could hear, as that was one of the last senses to go, and if he was listening now, he must be enjoying her reminiscing. I encouraged her to talk, and silently thanked the Lord for allowing me to be part of Mel's journey.

We called Jeff, as Mel's condition was rapidly declining, and he said he would hurry home. Sharon helped me adjust Mel's position and we raised the head of the bed up higher as she told me, "he breathes better that way." She gently washed his face and moistened his mouth with a swab to add to his comfort.

About this time Jeff arrived home. Sharon was teary and Jeff was comforting her as I told them Uncle Mel was getting ready to leave us pretty soon. Sharon and Jeff remained at the bedside stroking Mel, and telling him it was "Okay to go to Jesus," that they "would be okay." Again Sharon told Mel that "he was the best father anyone could have" and that she would give anything to "see his beautiful smile once more." What happened next astounded us all.

Mel sat up in bed, opened his eyes and looked at Sharon, and gave her the most beautiful smile I have ever seen. We looked at each other in astonishment, not believing what we had just witnessed. I marveled at

God's final gift to Sharon, a gift she would carry within her heart the rest of her life. I helped Mel to lie comfortably back against the pillows. No one said a word for a few moments, not wanting to break the spell. Sharon and Jeff just held each other and they both thanked Mel for this final gift.

Mel closed his eyes and shortly thereafter went peacefully to Heaven.

Later, after I left Jeff and Sharon with hugs, and they promised to let me know when little Mel arrived, I again marveled at the special moments I am allowed to share with patients and families. My prayer on my drive home was, "Thank you God for orchestrating this miracle for these special people." I am so humbled at all the expressions of love from our Lord that I see in my work every day.

Sharon and Jeff did send me a picture of 'little Mel," a perfectly beautiful baby boy. Somehow I think he will have his grandpa's smile, don't you?

Sam's Spirit

Linda was assigned to a patient named Sam from 8 am until 4 pm for imminent death. No other coverage was available. She arrived at the home and the patient himself opened the garage door for her because there was no one else there.

As I entered the home, I found Sam sitting at a small kitchen table. With his walker at his side and wearing only his underwear, he asked, "Are you here to clean my house?"

After a short conversation and orientation about "why the nurse is here," he kindly explained that he did not need to be nursed and that he had all his senses.

Sam allowed me to stay. I observed that Sam had deep mottling in both his legs from his knees down. He was alert and very clearly in charge. I assisted him to his chair in the living room and prepared breakfast at his request.

On the second day there was still only a day shift nurse available. Sam made arrangements for me to let myself in the garage with the remote control even though his granddaughter had decided to spend the night.

He fell during the night trying to get to the bathroom quickly. I discussed the idea of a bedside commode but Sam refused.

Sam insisted on going to his chair in the living room. (Sam's chair was one of those that has had a long life- very faded, very worn and very loved.) So that's what I helped him to do. By that time, Sam and I had reached an agreement. As long as Sam had his senses, I would take my cues from him. When the time came and Sam lost his senses, I could nurse him as needed.

Each day Sam continued to get weaker and was no longer eating. He still drank well but was getting short of breath just talking. He still desired to sit in his chair and walk to the bathroom even though both were getting more difficult for him.

On the fourth day, Sam was much weaker and the devastation was evident on his face. He finally agreed to oxygen, a wheelchair and a bedside commode and continued to sit in his favorite chair.

On the fifth day, I learned that Sam had taken to his bed about two hours after being assisted to his favorite chair. He never responded again and died peacefully later that morning. Sam left me with the greatest admiration and a greater respect of the human spirit.

Dignity and Self-Control

Patti Powell began as a volunteer for hospice before working as a nurse. Her story describes her last day with her first hospice patient and the importance of maintaining our dying patient's dignity and self-control.

In the late 80's I was assigned my first hospice patient after completing a 10-week hospice volunteer course with a hospice organization. She was a remarkable woman, my age, and dying of metastasized breast cancer. I went to her home and we visited on several occasions.

Linda, my patient, was single and lived alone in a small apartment in town. She had spent a month in a nursing home due to her illness and general debilitation but couldn't' stand the restrictions on her visitors. So she got an apartment, hired around-the-clock helpers and spent her last month there. She had parents in a nearby community but they were both in failing health so she didn't want to burden them with her illness. She was a schoolteacher and was evidently well loved by her colleagues because they called frequently and visited her in the evenings, as well.

I had been visiting her several times a week for a couple of weeks and when I came one Saturday she insisted on getting up, much to the chagrin of her caregiver. We helped her into her wheelchair, propped her and padded her as best we could and wheeled her into her kitchen. There she became the hostess/boss. She insisted that I was going to have breakfast with her that morning. I opened the refrigerator and got out a grapefruit sent to her recently by her brother while he and his family were visiting in Florida. Then she insisted that I have toast, coffee, etc. In the mean time she told her employee that she wanted some breakfast. It was very obvious that Linda had not eaten breakfast or much of anything else for a while.

The lady asked her what she wanted. She thought for a while and said, "Cereal. "

"What kind of cereal?"

"I don't know. Get them all out and I will decide."

The woman got out about four boxes of cold cereal from the cupboard. I was watching all of this with interest while preparing my breakfast, per Linda's instructions.

"I will have the Cheerios, thank you." Linda said. A bowl was placed on the table and with a great deal of ceremony Linda took what I remember as about six Cheerios into it. She told me to sit down and eat and as I ate my toast and grapefruit, she ate her breakfast.

It was one of those glorious spring days after a long winter in Indiana. We opened the kitchen window and listened to the birds singing, and smelled the fresh air. While I was there, a hospice nurse came by with a bunch of daffodils for Linda. We talked until she got tired and needed a nap. Then we took her back to her bed where I helped her get settled and then I said my goodbye.

That day was the first time Linda had been out of the bed in my presence since I had been seeing her. It was the first time I had ever heard her use her "boss" voice to anyone. It was the first time I had seen her put anything but medicine in her mouth. It was the last time I saw her alive.

Linda passed away early the next morning, Easter Sunday 1988. I will never forget her and the profound impression she made on my life. I will never forget the dignity she had and the lesson I learned about how important it is to be able to control something in your life, even if it is just having a bite or two of cereal when you want it.

<u>Gentle Reflections</u>: Quality of one's end of life is often in the eyes of the beholder. Understanding one's need for self-direction in care is paramount to preserving one's dignity. Having the freedom to choose how and when to go to the bathroom (even at the risk of falling), choosing where you want to sit, or even choosing what cereal you wish to eat are all simple human rights of autonomy. Often these needs go unrecognized in our efforts to protect our loved ones. Sometimes when this inherent need is not recognized, it may lead to frustration or even agitation for the one who is dying.

Run, Sarah, Run!

The following story is told by Linda Daniels who is a social worker for hospice. In her story she leads you through the progression of her patient Sarah's disease. Sarah sets a great example for all of us through her great sense of humor, the courage to fight to the end, and the never-ending love of living.

I had a sad day at hospice today, which is rare. I usually feel happy since I adore my co-workers and feel blessed with the opportunity to meet so many people associated with hospice, both patients and caregivers. I try to approach my patients with a happy heart. Of course, my heart gets sad sometimes but I try not to carry those sad feelings into the rest of my day.

The first day I met my patient Sarah she was in her condo overlooking the beach and ocean. What a wonderful lady! Sarah told me that she had been told she had cancer and did not have long to live. After some brief tears she said, "I don't believe them. I'm gonna fight it. I don't want to die! I love life. I want to live another ten years. There's so much I want to do." (Sarah was eighty-four!)

Sarah continued, "I go down to the pool, sit in the sun and imagine the sun is healing me. My friends laugh at me. They think it's silly that I do this." She said she dismisses them with a shrug and says, "Who cares what they think anyway?"

I think Sarah knew she was going to die and her will to live and fight was just a way to avoid looking directly at that exit door. There's a saying that reads, "One cannot look directly at death, just like one cannot look directly at the sun." (Author unknown)

I say, " Great, Sarah! You give it all the fight you have in you!" I'm sure that when I closed the door behind me at the condo, Sarah cried. Her condo must have been lonely at times. She loved it when her family came to help and visit.

Sarah became angry at her legs that wouldn't hold her up for very long. She fell a lot and she got so mad at those legs that she ordered them to work and then pounded on them with her fist. When people would reprimand her about falling and not following safety precautions, she just smiled and said, "I know, so what, I fell!"

Sarah told me many stories that made me laugh. She cried a little and then she laughed and her eyes sparkled. Her laugh was hardy and her eyes were full of mischief. She told me about a time she cooked up a plate of chicken livers with spaghetti and tomato sauce. She carried it into the dining room and fell. The food went all over the carpet. She pointed to the floor, "Can you believe it cleaned up so well? You can't even tell." She added, "I sat there and ate the chicken livers on the floor and when I was done...oh, they were good. I crawled over to a chair and eventually got myself up."

Another Sarah story is when she flew alone to Boston to visit her daughter. An airline employee wheeled her to the bus stop and said she was too busy to stay with her. The employee told her not to worry that the bus would be here soon. When a bus came, Sarah stood up, waved eagerly for the bus to stop, then fell back into the chair. The chair brake loosened and she went down an incline and ended up falling over the curb and bruising herself up good! She convinced those who gathered not to send her to the hospital because her daughter would take her the next day to be checked out.

A week went by and it was about time to leave her daughter's home. While sitting in the yard, she was bothered by "a big old dandelion staring at me." In this otherwise well-manicured yard, "I just had to pull it," she added. "I fell out of the chair, rolled down the hill and over the curb. At the hospital I was seen by the same doctor I'd seen a week earlier. He told me to be good at the airport, to promise him I'd sit still, eat a box of chocolates, read a magazine and just sit there.

One day, I visited Sarah who was now at an Assisted Living Facility. She was in bed, getting weaker, and no longer able to walk. I was happy to see her. I took her hand. She looked sad. She cried some and said she was getting worse.

Sarah said, "This is no way to live. I don't think I'm going to get better." Then she switched, "No, I'm gonna get better. I just need practice walking. How can I walk again without practice? Oh, I get so mad at these legs." Her eyes were beginning to sparkle again, illuminated by her spirit.

Sarah was getting animated and having fun. We put on her favorite Frank Sinatra CD. The first song always got to her. She'd say, "Oh, here it comes. Listen to this part, here it is, here it is." She would put her hand to her heart, sigh with ecstasy and say, "Isn't that beautiful?" Then she'd take her hand, raise it in the air and pound the air to the beat of the music. She was now lovin' life.

Aside from myself, I did not know that anyone reacted like that to music. In the backseat of my best friend Roxie's '64 Valiant in high school, a favored song would come on the radio and I'd holler, "Oh, my song…listen to this part…oh, I love this part." I'd grab my heart and say, "Oh, my God, isn't that fantastic?"

I am very familiar with that wild spirit in me that drives me to live my life with passion, joy and zest for this miracle called life. Sarah has that spirit too. She talks of her son (a speedboat racing champion), driving her on the beach in his Corvette convertible last year and loving it. I said to her, "Sarah, that is your style!"

Sarah answered, "You'd better believe it!" When she was seventy, her kids arranged for her and her husband to take a hot air balloon ride. She loved that too. I loved telling her how I celebrated my fiftieth birthday, riding in a racecar going 120 mph around the Daytona International Speedway.

Another time when I visited Sarah, she got off onto the detour from the fast lane to Heaven and declared she would fight dying to the end. I said, "Sarah, I love your spirit. You keep that spirit right to *the end. You know, some people think of dying as that last great adventure, an adventure into the unknown. I can picture you riding that wild stallion into the sunset."* She got a smile on her face as she pictured this and said, *"I rode horses when I was a child."*

One day I was leaving a restaurant and got into my car, I let myself cry. The mystery was why? It had to do with sadness for Sarah, who loved this life and was not done living. But her cancer had other plans for her. It's the image of that wild stallion and sunset that brought tears. Wild horses fascinate me and they represent for me the embodiment of the earth's spirit and all who live upon her. These horses are so beautiful when they run and it is so tragic when they are defeated. So, run Sarah run!

Lessons on Living from a Dying Man

Susan Burgess is a hospice social worker who has learned many lessons from her patients about living and dying. Here she shares those lessons everyone should heed.

John believed in living deliberately while dying, and enjoying it. As soon as he and his wife were confronted by the end of his life, they grieved openly and deeply for several days, and then made a pact to make every moment of every day joyful. Their delightful and all-consuming love for each other was a beauty to behold.

John realized that to understand and to enjoy this world, one has to assume full responsibility for one's self. When there was a problem, it mattered not whose fault it was. His only response was to find the solution and, if necessary, find help. He gave himself a feeling of awesome power to determine the quality of his life, including his end of life, and to exercise the precious freedom of choosing his reactions to each situation as it arose. As he determined the quality of his life and his relationships, he determined and established the meaning of his life. He was free.

In living life deliberately, he showed me that I have absolute and total choice over how I react to anything that happens: My life does not come with meaning or with value. The meaning and value of my life is exactly what I do with my life. He chose his reaction to the news that he was dying. He deliberately gave his life its special meaning.

He taught us that life becomes more pleasant, easy, and delicious once one's mortality is accepted. Death is a fact of life. Death itself is never the enemy. The enemy is the terrible pain and suffering that sometimes accompanies the process of dying, and that can be modified or even eliminated. And so he lived full of fun, humor, harmony and spirituality.

At the age of 76, incurably ill and enjoying life, John's goal was to die with dignity, peacefully and quietly at home with his wife in their bed. He did so a few short weeks after hospice care began. He said that the last part of his life was the most delightful, beautiful, loving, caring part of his entire existence.

Thank you, John, for the birth of my spirituality. Born of simple common sense, cutting out the myths and wishful thinking, and concentrating on what really is by living deliberately. With continual self-cultivation, I enjoy a life of joy and appreciation, balance and tranquility. Inspired by you, I take even more privilege and happiness in my work, helping other patients and *their loved ones embrace the end of life with the peace, comfort, joy, and the outlook that they choose.*

I Waited for You to Go

When you spend those final moments before death with your loved one, it will change you forever! You will realize that death really doesn't have to be as frightening as you may think. The uncertainty of the moment and the unknown events around death are two major reasons for fearing death. Your loved one may have unmet obligations and past guilt weighing them down which makes the uncertainties surrounding their death even more difficult to accept by them or you. Yet, you will not be afraid if you are prepared.

Emotions of all kinds will be exhibited in each one of us, whether we are in the bed or circled around the bed, because each one of us is unique. Some may be more talkative than others. Some will be sullen, stoic and tearful. No emotion will be right or wrong for the dying or their loved ones because of this uniqueness.

Our first thought about dying is perhaps that we don't want to die alone. It is human nature for us to not want to burden anyone with our care, yet very rarely does anyone want to die alone. However, a loved one may decide that the moment you leave their bedside is when they choose to take their last breath, as Vinny did one Saturday morning as told by Judy.

Vinny was a man of 54 years who had been battling pancreatic cancer for many years. When I arrived at his bedside, Vinny was in pain and having bouts of vomiting. His wife, Lila, was crying softly while caring and comforting Vinny.

Once Vinny's symptoms were under control, I spoke privately with Lila about how sick her husband was and that I was uncertain of the hour or day Vinny would die but knew it may be soon. Even though Lila cried harder, she knew the time was inevitable and Vinny was ready to die. She was exhausted after lovingly caring for Vinny's needs around the clock for days and felt she should take a few moments to herself to collect her thoughts. So Lila and I left shortly afterwards going separate ways, leaving Vinny with their daughter to care for him. Their daughter had spent many hours caring for her dad so everyone was comfortable leaving Vinny briefly.

Within one hour I was called back to Vinny and Lila's home. Within fifteen minutes of our leaving, Vinny had died. Lila was so distraught when I arrived! What I communicated to Lila was that it was probably Vinny's choice to die in her absence, realizing how difficult his moment of death would be on her. In those moments, her only comfort was knowing their daughter was with Vinny. Through tears, Lila shared many moments of joy she and Vinny had experienced in the last months, despite all the sorrow and hardship he endured.

Before I left Vinny and Lila's home, prayers were said as the family gathered with their pastor.

Happy Birthday

Linda's patient, Robert, was on Continuous Care for imminent death and had around-the-clock nurses in the home when available to keep him comfortable and to support the family. Nurses had been in the home for seven days. There was some unfinished business that the nurses and the family could not figure out that they felt kept Robert from passing peacefully.

"You know Dad always said he wanted to make it to ninety years old (Robert was 89)," his daughter said. Robert's 90th birthday was weeks away and there was just no way he could hang on that long.

Robert was growing weaker each day. His only response at the time was raising his eyebrows when you spoke to him, and he was only getting moisture through a toothette.

At change of shift on the seventh day, the daughter asked the 12 am nurse and I what we thought of her telling her dad that he made it, and singing the happy birthday song to him. We concluded it could do no harm and she told her dad, "You made it, Dad! Happy Birthday! You are ninety today!" Then she sang, "Happy Birthday to You." Robert died very peacefully approximately twenty minutes later.

A Lover Of Drama

This story was submitted by hospice nurse Judy Richotte. As her patient died, laughter and tears filled the room, just like her family expected it would!

I was with a patient who lived in a large beautiful home. Her hospital bed was in a large living room before the fireplace, where this woman with beautiful white hair and a beautiful face had been in a deep sleep for two days. She had been unresponsive, except to grimace when repositioned.

As the patient's time of death grew nearer, I gathered the family around the bedside where her four children, grandchildren, her sister, and her husband were all sitting on couches or chairs, waiting.

Finally the patient's oldest son rose, stood at the foot of the bed and said, "Mother, you always loved drama and being the center of attention at parties. Now is your big chance. We're all here and you have our undivided attention."

With these words, Barbara opened her eyes, looked around the room, smiled and said, "I love you all. See you in Heaven." She then died peacefully.

The family first laughed then cried and her son said, "Wasn't she great? That's Mom! How we'll miss her!"

<u>Gentle Reflections</u>: Often the dying need the completion of something before they can die peacefully. They may try to protect their loved one from seeing them die by holding on until another loved one is present or holding on until other family members have gathered together. The dying person at times appears to be able to stave off the actual death as if

waiting for something. This is when your knowledge of what was important to your dying loved one and careful listening will serve you well in providing what your loved one may need to have a peaceful death.

A Child's Collection from page 93

"Through the Eyes of a Child" from page 93

"Through the Eyes of a Child" from page 93

A Grandfather's House from page 103

A Flower for the Volunteers from page 111

Pet Power from page 143

Flowers from page 146

"The Hospice Story" from page 163

Chapter Four

Through The Eyes Of A Child

Often it takes a child to open our eyes to the things that really matter in this life, especially as we prepare for death. The simple things a child may wish for may take little thought and planning yet create the most precious and profound memories.

The Sad and Happy Times

Jay Lawrence Jr., at 8 years old, gave us permission to use his real name and his real story as told through his eyes as a child. Please read Jay's story exactly as he wrote it. We think he is a brave young man who loved his daddy very much. We know that Jay's daddy is very proud of him and would be pleased his son has contributed to this book. Read on about Jay's daddy…

The sad and Happy times

Hi my name is Jay Lawrence Jr.

I'm 8 years old. I'm the son of Jay Lawrence.

He passed away April 8th, 2002. My

daddy had cancer and that made him

very sick. The doctor said the cancer would

make him die and that made our

family very sad. I am glad that my

mommy and daddy told the truth about

my daddy having cancer. I know a little

bit about cancer but my sister doesn't

know about cancer. My Mommy and daddy

showed us pictures and read to us,
so we can know more about cancer.
My daddy didn't even look like he was dieing.
how could this be happening, I thought.
My daddy was a good person and very
good father. I was angry that my
daddy was dieing. My daddy got sick
and went into the hospital. It was the
chemo and radiation that made him sick.
It was like a war in his body. The chemo
was killing his blood cells. we went to
visit my daddy. I wanted my mommy
to make him better but she couldn't and

I was mad at her, she is a nurse and helps people but could not help my daddy. I hated her and wished she was the one dieing. later I told her that I loved her and I knew she was helping my daddy as best as she could.

The next morning my daddy called and wanted to know about hospice. my mommy told him what hospice was about. My daddy decided he didn't want to spend the little time he had left in bed or at the hospital. He didn't wont to be sick and weak any more. He called

hospice for help. Hospice helped my

daddy. They helped take his pain away so

he could do more things.

He was able to go to the beach agin.

My daddy loved the beach. we went to

gator land. we went out to dinner we spent

time friends and family I was happy that

my daddy was not in bed all the time. we

spent alot of time together. our funnest

times were riding the free wheeler out in the

woods. My daddy wanted to spend the weekend

with my sister and I at the beach.

My daddy didn't have the money to that.

In January 2002 Hospise made my

daddy's last wish come true hospice sent

us to a hotel on the beach for the weekend.

we played in the game room, the pool, and

the hottub was realy fun, we walked on the

beach, also drove up the beach. We had so

much fun that weekend. The hospice people

were nice and always will be my friends,

my daddy said, that he wouldn't know

what he would have done with out the
wonderful care of hospice. he also said,
they gave him his life back. hospice
allowed my daddy to stay at home and
have a quality of life. Thank you
hospice for making that possible. My Granny
came down from west virginia to care
for my daddy. My uncles cared for my daddy
too on April 8th, 2002 I was there at my
daddy's side laying in his arms He looked
very peaceful, he wasn't in any
pain. as he took his last breath, I wiped

my tears and Said, I don't need to cry any

more. my daddy went to Heaven.

In loving memory of my

daddy:

November 18, 1961 — April 8th, 2002

A Child's Courage and Strength

It is amazing to see children display such strength and grace in their characters at such young ages. Adults can learn so much from children especially those who face challenges in their young lives. The following story is about a brave young man named Claudius and an anonymous hospice caregiver who never forgot him.

This is a story about a 14-year-old young man I was fortunate to meet. He was a handsome, talented teenager known for his artwork. Claudius had bone cancer that had already taken one of his legs when it spread to his lungs. Hospice was called in because pain was a big problem. We worked quickly getting his pain under control. Trying to figure out what to do for a child was new for me. As soon as the pain was under control, Claudius had one goal and that was to go to school. He would have to walk about one and a half miles to get to school every day. I couldn't believe he would want to go to school with all he had going on! Every day he would get up, get himself ready and walk to school assisted only by his crutch. Some days he had a friend to walk with and some days he would be by himself. I would see him while I drove my own child to the same school. I even offered him a ride but he wouldn't take it. Where did he get this amazing inner strength?

One day my own 12-year-old started complaining about cleaning her room or some other small thing I asked of her. How dare she complain to me, when someone like Claudius would never complain no matter what he had to go through? He had a tremendous amount of courage and strength through his surgery, chemotherapy and the pain. He was never going to give up no matter what the obstacle.

I was in awe of the kind of person he was. I would try to tell my daughter that she had nothing to complain about and to look at what this child had to put up with. She would sometimes seem to understand but it didn't stop her from complaining. What I realized was that it did not really affect her, a child, too. I was the person who was really affected. What did I have to complain about when my child was healthy? My child would live to complain and/or accomplish things for many years to come. It was I who hugged my kid a little more each day and appreciated each day I was given.

It's been ten years since those days. My daughter is graduating from college. One day recently I happened to open the paper to the birth announcements, unusual for me since I almost never read the paper. There on the page was his name. I was certain that it was his sister, and she had named her baby after him. Even though I've thought of Claudius many times since his death, it was at this moment while reading the birth announcement that I felt the most joy. I am truly blessed to have been lucky enough to meet this fine young man and for the hope to meet another fine young man in the future.

The Death of Grandpa

Children aren't naturally afraid of death but take their cues from adults. They, like adults, don't want people they love to "go away." It is important to allow children to express their feelings when someone they love dies. The following story by Judy is about a little girl who loved her grandpa so much. She so sweetly, innocently, and clearly expresses in her own words the sorrow we all feel when someone dies.

   The little girl stood in the bedroom corner by her grandfather's bed. The lace curtains were blowing against her tiny shoulders as she stood nearly eye level with her grandpa as he lay still in his bed. So many family members were crying uncontrollably, not noticing the little girl standing so still by her grandpa. The huge teardrops rolled off her cheeks as she saw her final glimpse of Grandpa on this earth. "Grandpa!" she cried. "Don't leave me. Come back!"
   Then the hospice social worker walked softly to her and put her arms around her tiny shoulders. She tried hard to explain to such a young child why Grandpa died and what events are occurring around her. Perhaps through hospice bereavement counseling and support, she will be able to comprehend better why she has lost through death someone so precious to her.

<u>Gentle Reflections</u>: Children grieve in many different ways whether through crying, being very still, or exhibiting an extreme of emotions. Because children may need extra support after a loved one has died, many hospice organizations have counseling and bereavement centers and camps designed for them to aid in their sorrow and grief.

For Mothers and Sons

This is a touching story told by a hospice massage therapist, Suzanne DeWees, of a mother and her sons and how they found peace and comfort and, yes, joy in her passing.

A 48-year-old woman with end-stage liver cancer is very independent and has refused most hospice services other than her nurse. She has two sons, ages twelve and fourteen, and a live-in boyfriend who provides much needed support by primarily looking after the boys. She is very alone in her dying process and has expressed feelings of anxiety and guilt. A massage referral was made to me for spiritual distress.

I visited her on an early afternoon and had been given instructions to walk in through the garage since she was home alone. I found her standing in the kitchen with her back to me eating orange slices. Her breathing was labored with each step as she began the strenuous journey back to her bedroom. She resettled herself in her king-sized bed and began to speak about her illness. I noticed her hesitancy to make eye contact with me. She showed me her extended belly and her anguish found a voice, "Look at my poor body."

We arranged her comfortably in her bed so that I could begin long, slow backstrokes. She was like a small, frightened child. After fifteen minutes, she made eye contact with me and spoke through deep, releasing sobs, "My mother is losing me. I am her only child. I feel so terrible that she is losing me. There is nothing I can do to help her." She cried and cried, soaking her pillow as I stroked her and softly repeated, "I am so sorry."

She and I had many such heart-to-heart sessions where she spoke about her dying process and I listened. She was a very sensuous woman, and I felt that the power of touch brought her in touch with her deepest feelings. As she felt comforted by my touch, she named her fears, moved through deep emotions and relaxed into a deeper, quieter place in her heart.

As our sessions together softened the armor around her loneliness, she gathered courage. One day as I stroked her arms, she whispered to me that she was not afraid of dying. She spoke of the belief about returning "to the ocean of light." The massage session offered the privacy and the quiet for her to express her spiritual needs as well.

Near the end of her life, she told me that her youngest son had laid down with her in her bed the night before which he hadn't done since he was very young. She recounted the great joy they shared in those few moments with their arms wrapped around each other.

A few days later, when I went to say good-bye to her, knowing that her death was imminent, I spoke to her son saying that his mom had told me how much she had appreciated the hugs he had given her.

That night she died, and the nurse told me that it was an exquisite, peaceful passing. First, her youngest son climbed into bed next to her, then her oldest son climbed in on the other side. She was able to nod her head. She died with her children holding her and her boyfriend at her bedside watching over all.

I will always hold her love and gratitude in my heart for having responded to her deepest needs.

Losing A Child

"How could it happen this way? We are supposed to go first!" So often those are the words of the weak and frail elderly parents of middle-aged children as they deal with the imminent death of their sons and daughters. I wonder how they will survive their loss. Then a visit to a dying child and her mother reminds me, Judy.

As Elizabeth sits next to her adult child who lies dying, the tears stream down her face. In my mind, I picture Elizabeth as a young mother with this same child cuddled up in bed with her. Then just when I thought the mother's strength to carry on was gone, she gently reaches for her tattered Bible and begins reading the 23rd Psalm to her daughter. This amazing mother found great strength and joy in that moment of death by sharing those tender words of love with her child as she had done many years before.

Christopher Landon Touches Death

Michael Landon's son, Christopher, was sixteen years old when his famous father died. He described, through David Kessler, the effect his father's loss had on him and what he gained through it. Please read Christopher's own words.

"Noticing many of my fears fade after he died got me thinking about death in general. When you love someone and they die, you form your first relationship with death. You come close to it, you are less afraid of

it because you've been with it. I was with my father when he was dying, and after he passed away. I touched death and it touched me."

A Little Boy Who Gives Me My Smile Back

JoAnne King is a hospice social worker who may remind you of a Disney character. At least a four-year-old little boy thought so.

When I meet people outside of work and tell them I work with a hospice program, the response is usually, "You're such a good person. I don't think I could do that kind of work. You people are angels." Other hospice workers tell me they get the same kinds of reactions. While I do appreciate the goodwill and respect others have for hospice work, I would dare say that the grace we receive from doing this work far outweighs any benefits we could ever provide. One experience in particular always reminds me of this.

Years ago as a field social worker, I helped care for an elderly woman who lived with her adult son, his wife, and their four-year-old son. Following the patient's death, I made a bereavement visit to the family. I sat at the kitchen table talking with the daughter-in-law. Throughout our conversation her son, Bobby, would run up and hug me, smile, then run back to where he had been playing. He did this a few times which I found unusual because he had only met me briefly during a previous visit and at that time seemed shy and reserved. Finally his mother asked him, "Bobby, what on earth are you doing?" He looked up at us with the most precious blue eyes, gave a mile-wide smile, pointed at me and said, "Look Mama, it's Pocahontas!"

His mother turned beet red, and told me that Bobby had recently watched the Disney movie "Pocahontas." I have a fairly dark complexion and at the time of this visit had long, straight, dark hair. Bobby apparently believed I was THE Pocahontas, who had come especially to see him. His mother seemed incredibly embarrassed and repeatedly apologized to me. My response was, "Ma'am, that was about the nicest thing anyone could ever say to me."

I've shared this story over the years with friends and co-workers. It never fails to bring a smile to their faces, or to mine. Last Christmas, a co-worker brought me a framed picture from the movie showing Pocahontas paddling down the river. She found it at a garage sale and thought that I should have it. It hangs in my office now so that daily I am reminded of two things:

1. The world is a wonderful, magical place when viewed through a child's eyes.
2. When I'm having a bad day, folks are upset with me, or things just aren't going right, I remember that somewhere out there, a little boy thinks I'm THE Pocahontas. And then I smile. Again.

Make A Wish

Many hospice organizations and special foundations provide final wishes or gifts, whether it is a special event ticket, a trip to Disney World, or a shopping spree for your loved one. Author Marie De

Hennezel shares a short story from her book, *Intimate Death: How The Dying Teach Us How To Live,* about two extreme wishes from one special boy.

A 12-year-old boy with leukemia had a wish before dying and that was to meet the Dalai Lama, and he did. When the boy was asked what he needed most in regard to his illness, he said, "What I need is for people to treat me as if I weren't ill. For them to laugh and have fun with me and just be natural."

Dying with Joy and Sorrow

Chapter Five

Volunteers For Hospice

For many years volunteers have been the backbone of many organizations around the world. Hospice is no exception to the greatness of their volunteers! Volunteers for hospice perform many varied duties from meal preparation, feeding patients, transporting patients from doctor's offices to salon appointments, reading stories, writing letters, assisting with basic personal care, performing light secretarial duties, managing fund-raisers or quietly sitting at the bedside of the dying holding their hand. This world is a more glorious place because of the loving and self-sacrificing volunteers who are just what the doctor *didn't* order!

The Lady with the Long Red Hair

Lou Arnold is an aide who works in a hospice care center. She has personally cared for hundreds of patients who are dying and understands that each death is special. Lou listens to patient's wishes and honors them, no matter how big or how small. The following story is how Lou listened to a patient whose dignity was found in her long red hair and how she connected her to a volunteer who made a special, treasured moment in the dying woman's life.

Some time ago an older lady was admitted to the Hospice Care Center. We were told that she had been living alone and was not living in favorable conditions. She had no close family members, just cats and dogs in a meager home that she called her own. Up to this point, she had refused any help, but her disease had progressed so rapidly that she relented. Needless to say, her body was just skin stretched over bones, but what got our attention more so was the condition of her hair. It was all matted with rusty hairpins holding her long red hair in some kind of a twist off her shoulders.

After she was made comfortable, she was asked if we could bathe her and wash her hair and perhaps cut out some of the tangles. She looked up at us and stated, "You can do anything you want to me, but don't cut my hair." With all her poverty and terrible sickness, her hair was all she had left – long red hair. That was her decision and we abided.

Because of her weakened condition, she was given a bed bath and shampoo but the tangles and matted hair still remained. In fact, they were more apparent than ever. Then Valerie, a volunteer, appeared and was asked if she felt like taking on the challenge of removing the tangles from this new patient's hair.

Her first concern was the discomfort this would cause the patient. A way was worked out where the tangles could be combed out comfortably, but it was going to be a very tedious process. Valerie eagerly started the task at hand.

A little later I checked in on her and found Valerie, with big tears running down her face, pulling tangles out of long strands of the patient's hair. Immediately I asked Valerie if she was all right. She said, *"The patient relaxed and fell asleep, seemingly enjoying all the care and attention. But while standing here, I have been praying for her and in a sense have felt all the pain and loneliness this lady has gone though."*

I gave Valerie a big hug and left her to finish her task. Meanwhile, someone else found a pretty blue gown and a piece of ribbon to gather up that red hair and get it off her shoulders. Hours later when Valerie was finished and we placed the gown and ribbon on the patient, there was a total transformation. Her long hair was like a cloud on the pillow. But more than a transformation of looks took place. Valerie connected with this patient in a special spirit.

The very next day our special little lady with the long red hair died and she went with all the dignity that was possible! Thank you, Valerie and God bless you.

Lessons In Listening

Working with children who are dying takes special courage. They can be our best teachers, ever. Susan Kaufmann is a hospice volunteer who developed her honed listening skills early in life by listening to a child.

While in college, I was working in Oncology in Philadelphia Children's Hospital. One day while in a patient's room working as a parent counselor, the following occurred with my patient, who was a thirteen – year-old boy. He was extremely ill and additionally nauseated from treatment. He weakly asked his mother, "Mom, am I going to die?"

I thought, "Oh my, what should I do or say?"

Then his mother calmly said, "Son, we are all going to die but none of us know where or when." What courage she had and it was my first lesson in learning to wait and LISTEN! What an insightful, honest lady and how hard that must have been for a mother to say. I quickly learned the value of honesty and that there was nothing to say or give but complementary support.

Gentle Reflections: Moments of conversation with the dying should be filled with honesty and respect for their right-to-know. Often our patients sense their decline in health and drawing closer to death even though the end of life has not been discussed.

For Her I Will Endure

The following story is written by Edward J. Cooper, a very dedicated volunteer for hospice. Ed reminds us that our patients will do all they can and endure whatever they need to so others wishes can be fulfilled.

Several years ago I was assigned a patient (we will call John), a gentle man, who had a life threatening blood disorder. As we were introduced, he indicated that his time was down to about three weeks.

John was married but he and his wife had not been blessed with children so he was quite alone. The aloneness was not due to choice but to his deteriorating health. His beloved wife had succumbed several years previously to Alzheimer's disease and she was in a home that offered full nursing care.

During the course of his care, John's time increased to three months and as we had made a number of trips to the hospital for transfusions, we developed a personal relationship. The three months raced by and the blood transfusions increased until the time came when there could be no more. John's doctor suggested he transfer to the Hospice Care Center and John called me to ask if I would drive him there.

This is a very emotional time for a patient as they leave their home for probably the last time but true to his nature John was not thinking of himself but of his wife who would soon be left without him. During our ride over to Port Orange, John extracted a promise from me that I was to do my best to keep him alive until the first of the coming month.

Curiously I asked why this date. John explained that his social security checks were dedicated to his wife's care and there is a ruling that an entire month's check must be returned unless the recipient lives through the end of the month.

Visits to the Hospice Care Center increased until I was seeing John a couple of times a day. Each time with his best smile and quiet manner, he reminded me of my promise. When John went into a coma about the 28th of the month, I continued to visit several times a day and night and while there I would remind John of the exact date and time of month. Even though there was no response, my training had been that all patients could be aware of voices and understand what was being said around them, so on the last evening of the month at about 11:00 pm, I spoke to John and said, "John, you have made it. It is almost midnight and in just a few hours you can know that you have succeeded in your quest to live through to the end of *the month." I then went home and upon returning the next morning was told by the nursing staff that John had died at 2:00 am.*

John was an amazing man, and I have never forgotten him. He proved to me that even in a coma one's life is still worth a fight. If one cannot fight for one's own life then perhaps the will to accomplish a goal for a loved one proves to be a good reason.

This was four years ago and the memory of those several months with John remain with me as a powerful reminder of the strength of fighting for one's own goals.

Farewell, John. We remember with joy your life and it's last purpose.

A Visit From South Africa

Suzanne DeWees was part of a grand plan to bring together a father, who was dying, and his son who lived thousands of miles apart.

We get very close to families in hospice. As they keep a bedside vigil, they invite us into their hearts and we all participate in the sacred journey of dying and death.

One day last September while I was massaging a patient, he talked about his life and began to choke and sob when he mentioned his son, the captain of a boat in Richard's Bay, South Africa. I asked him to tell me about his son and he pointed to a fax, with faint print, that was push-pinned into a cork bulletin board. He spoke in despair, "My son sometimes gets to shore to call me or fax me, but I can't call him. And I know I'll never see him again."

Indeed the worn and faded fax had been sent from South Africa and I noticed a return fax number and an indistinguishable e-mail address. I encouraged my patient to dictate a letter that I would return to the one-month-old fax number (not knowing if his son was still moored in Richard's Bay). So he dictated heartfelt words telling his son how proud he was of him, how much he admired him and that he missed him. When I faxed the dictated letter to his son, I included my e-mail address, knowing that cyberspace is everywhere… even out to sea.

Within a few days, I received an email from his son. He had gone ashore, hitched a ride into the local town, and retrieved his dad's fax. Back at sea, his ship-to-shore radio had e-mail capabilities. He was so pleased! He began to send daily messages to his dad and the energy between the two began to draw us all in. "Read today's e-mail," the patient would tell a night-shift nurse or the smiling volunteer who brought his breakfast.

One day his son e-mailed me and inquired: if he was able to get to Melbourne Beach where he had friends he could stay with, how far was the Hospice Care Center? Was there any public transportation? A plan for his son to come to see his father quietly unfolded in cyberspace and soon his father, who had noticeably declined from the disease progression, was told, "Your son is on his way." The Hospice Care Center staff hoped that he could stay alive until his son arrived and indeed, he hung on "for dear life."

Thirty-two hours after his son left Richard's Bay, a hospice volunteer and his wife were waiting at the Orlando International Airport. The Social Worker Department, the Volunteer Department and the Care

Center Administration had together made plans for his housing and local transportation.

Reunited after four years, the energy between the two was delightful and the patient miraculously lived on for twenty-eight days while his son visited. Their time together included watching football games and telling stories in the middle of the night. It was a true family reunion!

The volunteers networked a support system for his son while he was here away from his wife and friends. Volunteers invited him out to lunch, over for dinner or to the beach for a walk. He became close to the many, many Hospice Care Center staff and volunteers who cared for his dad with affection and love.

When it came time for him to return home, hospice volunteers offered to take him back to the Orlando airport. Many people were present to say good-bye. Many of us cried. Several days later, he e-mailed us letting us know he arrived home safely. Our Care Center chaplain returned an e-mail telling him the details of his dad's peaceful passing.

One Christmas

Meredith Iannarelli recruits and trains new volunteers to work in various capacities within the hospice organization. She proves that it is better to give than to receive as she and her volunteers for hospice discovered.

The Christmas season always brings out the hopes and wishes of all of us that we can in some small way positively impact another's life. I cannot go another Christmas without thinking of one of our patients and the experience we had with him and his family. This gentleman came to our program in November. Diagnosed with mouth and throat cancer and only in his forties, he was unable to work to support his family. His wife was employed but with three young sons there was not enough money to meet the daily expenses, much less afford Christmas for the children. It looked like a bleak holiday for all of them.

He told his social worker that his last wish was for his boys to have some sort of Christmas. She passed this information along to the volunteer department, and although it was nearly December, we said we would try to do something. I asked his wife to have the three boys, ages nine, seven, and six write letters to Santa. The boys were told to ask for everything they wanted and Santa would fulfill as many of the requests as he could. The letters were delivered to the volunteer department and volunteers cut out paper angels, one for each of the toys requested. Armed with these angels, we went to the December staff meeting, explained our patient's last wish and asked if anyone wanted to take an angel and buy that gift. It was very close to Christmas by this time and we hoped that at least a few of the boys' wishes would be met.

The response was overwhelming! Not only was every angel taken by a staff member, there were not enough to go around! Staff members came up to me afterwards and said they would buy something extra for the boys. Everyone wanted to help.

Christmas Eve was exciting and busy as volunteers lovingly wrapped each present. One of our chaplains, dressed in a Santa suit lent to us by a volunteer, drove his van while our social worker and I, dressed as elves, rode along as helpers. We had such a good time driving to their house in our van full of toys and bikes. We waved to everyone we saw on the way, wishing them a Merry Christmas.

As we approached the dirt road our patient lived on, we saw a gaunt man with a handkerchief covering his face stooped over, but determinedly standing at the edge of the road. As we neared, he weakly raised his arm to wave us down and we stopped. It was our patient, who, although very weak, was so excited he had to walk down to make sure we found his road and his home. He led us to his mobile home, his gait a proud father's walk as he brought Santa to his children.

The boys scrambled all over the van, crowding in front of the door, shrieking with excitement. Their eyes grew bigger each time another present was unloaded and ran up and down the steps to the house, their anticipation at a crescendo. I watched our patient through all of the chaos, and although only his eyes were showing, the emotions he felt were so evident. His eyes glowed and sparkled with such a pure joy that no words from him were necessary. He hoarsely but patiently told the boys they had to wait until their mother got home from work before they could open any of the presents. He wanted her to be part of the special Christmas.

Our patient died in January but before he did, he told our social worker how grateful he was for that last Christmas. Little did he know how I carry the look in his eyes in my heart, and how every Christmas I think of him and his love for the family he was leaving behind.

Eight Small Words

Sometimes, when we least expect it, a patient will say something so simple, so sincere and so powerful that the moment will be remembered for a lifetime. The adventure of becoming a hospice volunteer is filled with many "stop me in my tracks" moments. The moment was made up of eight small words as spoken to a volunteer who wishes to remain anonymous.

Being a fairly new volunteer with hospice, I was truly taken aback one morning after assisting a patient with his breakfast when he said, "I'm really going to miss all of you." I had to fight back the tears. What greater appreciation can we receive?

Maya Angelou Remembers

When loneliness bears heavy on those grieving the loss of a loved one, rejuvenation is taking place in one's mind and soul. Our tender memories replay quietly in our mind and the ache deep in our soul begins to ease. Ever so slowly a smile evolves as we remember them well. The great poetry of Dr. Maya Angelou gently reminds us that our joyful memories will continually replenish us even in times of pain and sorrow as this excerpt from *I Almost Remember* depicts.

On late evenings when
quiet inhabits my garden
when grass sleeps and
streets are only paths for silent
mist

I seem to remember

Smiling

by Dr. Maya Angelou

Chapter Six

Complementary Therapies

Traditional, modern medicines and procedures can cure, extend our lives and help us live productively when our bodies have a chronic, compromising disease. Yet, what heals our spirits, our souls? What can bring us peace and comfort? Complementary therapies such as massage, aromatherapy, music, guided imagery, acupuncture, and touch when used with traditional, modern medicine can help to heal our bodies, minds, and spirits.

The Deep

The power of touch is eloquently described in Gail E. Stark's poetry. Gail is a strong believer in touch therapy as her patients confirm, "You're better than any pill they give me."

I fill my hands with ocean waves…
Caress your feet with swirling tidal pools.
I drop rose petals on your back…
Blanket you with rainbow quilts of
        Brilliance beyond words.

There are no words as I massage you…
Quiet touch--silent spaces--
Wandering the Elysian fields,
        Our hands entwined,
I glimpse your soul's perfection.

Finding Peace

Chris Garden tells this poignant story about her special patient with amyotrophic lateral sclerosis (ALS). Through her use of healing touch, her patients and their families find peace and comfort in their final days together.

One day I received a phone call at my office from a very pleasant sounding woman who asked me questions about hospice and the services we offered. I explained our services as she had requested, only to hear her reply that the reason she was curious was because she had been diagnosed with ALS a few months prior and she was making plans for her future care needs. I offered to make a home visit and talk with her about her wishes, as to what she does and does not want done to her, medically speaking. She was delighted that I would come to her home and speak with her and her husband. Little did I know that this would become a very special relationship for both of us. I will call this "special soul" Jennifer to protect her identity.

During my first visit, I again explained hospice services to Jennifer and her husband. We talked about many topics that day including important, future medical choices. Jennifer and her husband had tears in their eyes discussing some of these things, as is certainly understandable, but they also told me how glad they were that they had the opportunity to talk about and be informed about all of these things. Education empowers people.

During our discussion, I found out that Jennifer wasn't ready for hospice yet. I explained my role as a palliative care nurse and offered to keep in touch with her, offering education where she felt it was needed. I explained "palliative" meant to bring comfort where there was no cure and that it was a holistic approach to health care incorporating the body, emotions, mind and spirit. I further explained the use of complementary therapies and their usefulness in symptom management as a part of palliative care. Both she and her husband voiced an approval of and a desire for complementary therapies to be included in Jennifer's treatment. I explained that I am certified in healing touch and interactive guided imagery and would like to offer these therapies as part of our palliative care visits. They accepted and were thrilled that these therapies were available.

I began to visit Jennifer weekly. She would begin our visit talking about her decline since the last visit and what it was like to have a progressive paralysis that for her began at the feet and worked its way up. To see her week after week declining to the point she couldn't even scratch was heartbreaking.

Here was a young woman, sharing her dreams that she wouldn't get to fulfill, sharing her fears about this invader to her body that had stripped her of her life. I looked at her and thought, "How courageous." Jennifer had the kind of energy that just touched your heart. One time during a healing touch treatment, she had her eyes closed in delight and relaxation and my eyes teared up in compassion and love for this brave soul. After the treatments, she would always thank me and tell me how much she looked forward to my visits. She said she thought that God had sent her an angel to help her deal with all of this and I thought how God had sent me an angel to teach me courage, peace and acceptance.

Jennifer's decline was very evident. I asked her if she was now ready to go on hospice care and she said yes. We obtained an order from her physician that day and signed her to hospice the next day. She was already in need of oxygen for breathing comfort and was thankful that hospice could get it so readily for her. Her husband was thankful for the emotional support that hospice offered, as he was becoming exhausted from constant care twenty-three hours a day, seven days a week.

I continued to visit Jennifer and give healing touch treatments with techniques that would make her body more comfortable and clear and relax her still very sharp thinking mind, hoping that she could find some peace in sleep. I also included guided imagery and aromatherapy, all with gentle beautiful music in the background. The last time I saw Jennifer, I ended our treatment with my usual gentle kiss to her forehead and, "Get some peaceful sleep."

She responded with, "I love you."

I returned with, "I love you, too," and my usual hand-blown kiss to her and, "I'll see ya' next week, my dear."

I never saw Jennifer again. On the morning of my next visit, Jennifer spread her wings. Her loving husband and two daughters who whispered, "We love you and it's okay to go," surrounded her. Jennifer died peacefully just after that. I kept my usual appointment and stopped by to see the family. They were so thankful for hospice and all of the support and comfort they offered, and to me for the weekly treatments that Jennifer loved so much and looked forward to. These treatments afforded her the opportunity to find some peace and acceptance in her death. I felt a real loss and still do. She was wonderful and I loved her but I'm

*glad she is no longer suffering. I said my good-byes
and sent her my love along her path.*

*After Jennifer's death, I am thankful that God
sends me such wonderful people to learn from. They all
have their special gifts to offer us if we are aware
enough to perceive it, learn from it, and be thankful for
those gifts.*

The Many Benefits of Massage Therapy

Suzanne DeWees leads us through her patient's
journey with Lou Gehrig's disease, describing how
valuable the power of touch can be.

*A forty-nine-year-old patient with amyotrophic
lateral sclerosis (Lou Gehrig's disease) had lost all
muscle movement in his legs, lower torso, left arm and
hand. He had limited use of his right arm and hand and
is able to speak with a labored breath. He was at home
with his family members caring for him. The hospice
interdisciplinary team visited daily. A hospice massage
referral was made to provide comfort, reduce anxiety
and improve overall circulation.*

*I began with two visits per week, and provided
leg and foot, and arm and hand massages. Although
the patient did not have muscle control of his legs and
feet, he could feel the sensations of my touch. He got
to know our routine, yet he repeatedly said to me in a
whisper, "Massage my legs." I felt that his making the
request gave him a tiny bit of control over his body. He
reported enjoying the sensations of the blood
circulating in his legs and feet.*

Once I gained his trust, I began to work on his back and neck. He liked to sit up in his hospital bed, with his one working hand holding a rail that supported his upright position. In order for me to massage him, he would allow me to support his sitting posture by resting his head on my shoulder, with my shoulder supporting his body, as I massaged his back.

He completely surrendered to my care of him during a hospice massage session. I felt the preciousness of that surrender and the gift of intimacy. He relaxed so deeply into those massage strokes, that his labored breath would lengthen and his ability to speak improved.

On one occasion, a Continuous Care nurse watched me give him massage. She asked for some instruction, stating that she could also provide him with those same long strokes to help him sleep. He gave us a precious smile as we both massaged his feet.

One morning, I brought a blend of oils, including some essential oil to provide a pleasant aroma. I massaged his entire body, with extra attention to his neck muscles, which were considerably weaker due to the disease progression. He hadn't spoken during the massage. He was very peaceful and was naturally withdrawing into a deep stillness.

Although I don't usually massage a patient daily, I knew that he was tremendously comforted by massage and it was helping him to face his approaching death. He had told me earlier that he felt more peaceful after each massage. As I was preparing to leave, I told him, "I will be back tomorrow." He looked at me and faintly asked, "What time?" His wife told me, when she walked me to my car that those were the only words he had spoken in two days.

I knew that his massages had been an essential aspect of his care that helped make life worth living

*through the very difficult disease progression of ALS.
He had enjoyed looking forward to each session. She
also felt supported by my coming to their home and
providing massages. She reported that he slept
soundly afterwards and needed less anxiety
medications on the day of massage. She felt comforted
by the look of peace on his face afterwards.*

*When I went back to the house the next day, a
black wreath hung on the door. He had died during the
night. I felt a great loss. His wife thanked me at his
memorial service for caring for him with such great
love. She also told me, through an avalanche of tears,
that she had noticed how wonderfully soft and fragrant
his body was when she had kissed him good-bye.*

The Power of Thirty Hands

Fifteen massage therapists discovered how to
ease the fear of death through the power of touch and
song, as told by Suzanne DeWees.

*One of Dr. Christopher Alexander's patients won
our hearts. I don't think he meant to. He just had this
way of being in love with life and he extended that love
all around him.*

*I first met him in the Regional Oncology Center
at Halifax Medical Center in Daytona Beach. He would
come once a week for his chemotherapy treatment. He
loved to get a foot massage on that day. My patient
was young, around thirty-five, and had a fairly carefree
attitude, not letting the disease progression dampen his
spirits. Amy, one of the volunteer massage therapists,
really knew how to laugh with him*

Over time, he was admitted several times to the hospital's oncology floor. Whenever he returned, he seemed to feel safe and content to be cared for by the oncology nurses. They attended to him with special, very tender and loving care. He looked forward to the massage sessions from Amy (his new buddy), Linda, Bruni, Marty and Rita. These massage therapists spoke of how he returned the gift of touch by touching their hearts. His presence beamed love and a playful sense of humor.

One week the Daytona Beach Community College (DBCC) Therapeutic Massage students began an internship at Halifax Medical Center in Palliative Massage. They had assignments throughout the hospital and massage student intern Ramiro was assigned to my patient. When Ramiro and I walked into the patient's room, the patient was visibly upset over his disease progression and loss of mobility. He vented his anger in a shrill, childlike voice. Ramiro went to work massaging his back, arms, legs, hands and feet. By the end of the session, the patient was very relaxed and very *peaceful.*

Two students teamed up and went another night. Soon all the students knew about him from our internship discussions. They knew he was dying and they knew he was somewhat alone in the world.

On the last night of the internship, the students, their teacher and I held class in the conference room with time for evaluations, questions and answers, etc. The students felt that we shouldn't leave the hospital without seeing our patient, for they knew it would be their last opportunity to connect with him. Their teacher agreed. So at 9 pm we crowded into the elevator and went to his room, all fifteen of us. With a student massaging each hand, and a student at each foot, the rest of us sang to him, "Swing low, sweet chariot, coming for to carry me home," a traditional spiritual song by Harry Thacker Burleigh.

I knew from my hospice work that patients love to be sung to; it's reminiscent of lullabies, a mother's love, and God's protection. Our young, tired friend began to sing along with us. His weary head resting on the pillow as he sang the words, "I looked over yonder and what did I see, coming for to carry me home." When we ended, he thanked us with smiles and love beams. We quietly said goodnight and tiptoed out of the room as he took refuge in God's love.

When his mother arrived from out of town and was at his bedside, the angels must have known he was ready. He died that night. The care of his doctor, nurses, palliative massage volunteers and DBCC therapeutic massage interns had all comforted him on his difficult journey of dying. In return, all had met a person who they'll never forget.

While he was here, our friend shared some of his feelings about the palliative massage program: "This gets better every time. Rita gave me a very good sense of peace and tranquility. She was very healing. Amy really feels like a friend, talking to you along the way and caressing your pain at the same time. Palliative Care can take the blues away, even if only for a moment. Thanks."

Gentle Reflections: The power of touch is not found only through the professional hands of a therapist, but can be just as powerful and comforting as touching and holding one's hand as they approach death.

Finding Solace In Silence

Sometimes a patient's death is not as predictable as we may think. That is what Suzanne DeWees discovered after giving a very comforting massage to her hospice patient.

The 68-year-old woman with end-stage chronic obstructive pulmonary disease (COPD) resided in the Hospice Care Center. She was very quiet and reserved, anxious, and isolated. She had few visitors and no family. A massage referral was made to me to reduce respiratory distress and to provide an accompanying presence to reduce fear and anxiety.

I began with two sessions per week to increase ribcage mobility, ease neck stiffness and stimulate the respiratory system. Following chest tapotement, I offered a foot massage to help alleviate stress. I felt very tender towards this patient, as I do with all COPD patients, having seen my mother live short-of-breath for many years.

She enjoyed and benefited from our massage sessions. She especially enjoyed having me play soft, relaxing music during our time together and being led in a relaxation exercise. She trusted me and expressed renewed faith in God's will after our sessions. Often we would repeat the 23rd Psalm together while holding hands before I would leave. "The Lord is my shepherd, I shall not want."

On one particular day, the nurse called me stating that my patient was unusually agitated and restless. Many patients have good days and bad days, during the end stage of their illness. I am frequently asked to treat restlessness with slow strokes and a calm, reassuring presence. While massaging her she began to cry, confiding in me that she had spoken very harshly to one of the nurses several days before. She went on to say that in the entire course of her illness she had not taken her private upsets out on another person. She felt that she had indeed let herself and her God down. As she cried, I soothed her and stroked her with great tenderness.

She had a beautiful hand-blown glass statue of the Virgin Mary next to her bed from which she drew strength. We prayed together for the divine Mother's presence. Together we found solace in a deep, gracious silence as I continued to comfort her with my touch. As I ended the session she said, "Thank you. I feel better. I have forgiven myself."

When I went to visit her the next day, her bed was empty. I went to the nurse's station asking if she had been moved to another room. I was told that she had died very peacefully two hours after our last session, although she had not shown the usual physical signs of imminent death.

As I reflected on the time we spent together, I felt I had been a part of God's immense grace in dying. Her ability to forgive herself provided the spiritual energy needed to "let go" as she died with a peaceful heart.

Dying with Joy and Sorrow

Chapter Seven

Make Me Laugh

Does laughter have its place when facing the end of one's life? We do not wish to imply that dying is a laughing matter, just that there are some instances where it does have its place. As you will see in the following stories, laughter can take the edge off a very difficult time in people's lives. Laughter is part of the joy often seen in life review, and it can provide comfort when saying goodbye. Some even see humor as healing as you will read in an excerpt from Michael Landon.

Heavenly Laughter in Little Joe's Little House

When the words "Little Joe," "Little House on the Prairie" and "Highway to Heaven" are heard, nearly everyone thinks of Michael Landon. What some may not remember is Michael's valiant fight against cancer, dying at the young age of 54 in 1991. What Michael taught his fans and loved ones about the importance of humor and confronting one's fear of death will last a lifetime! The following excerpt by Aileen Joyce describes how strongly Michael Landon believed in humor as healing:

"Michael had read several books on how humor can have a positive effect on ill health. So he had rented comedy videos and cartoons and, together with his family, had watched them hour upon hour, laughing at the comedic high-jinks of everyone from Laurel and Hardy to Steve Martin."

In Michael's own poignant words as written by Harry and Pamela Flynn, Michael says, *"Remember me with smiles and laughter, for that is how I will remember you all. If you can only remember me with tears, then don't remember me at all."*

Dixie and Ray

After ringing the doorbell, a shaky voice from deep inside the home yelled, *"Come in!"* After pushing the door open, I yelled in, *"It's Judy from hospice."* Then I could hear the familiar rumble of an oxygen machine. My eyes automatically looked to the floor. The oxygen tubing was easy to spot against an old green, shag carpet. As I followed the snake-like pathway, my steps led me to a bedroom in the west side of the home. The setting sun filled the room, spilling onto my patient lying in the hospital bed.

"I'm so glad you came," the voice of my dying patient whispered. Behind the whisper lay a frail lady named Dixie who had fought long and hard against lung cancer. Her disease had weakened her body but not her wonderful spirit for living!

"Hi, Dixie! What a gorgeous, sunny day!" I said.

"Yes, it was until I fell," she whispered.

Just then Ray, Dixie's husband, entered our little world of sunshine. "She sure took a tumble!" Ray exclaimed. "I found her on the kitchen floor. She's never fallen like that before."

My heart started to squeeze as I was aware that certain facts will need to be discussed before I left Dixie and Ray. They both said nearly in unison, "Please be open and tell us both what to expect. We've always been up front and honest with each other."

After a tearful discussion about the expectations of Dixie's decline, as she grew closer to death, Ray walked me to the front door I had entered an hour earlier. As we walked along the snake-like path, Ray told me how much in love he and Dixie were, "Even after all these years we make every moment as happy as we can. We love to laugh even when times are tough."

Again my patient and her loved one encouraged me, reminding me that there are lots of good times despite the bad. Every moment of every day is to be savored and shared. Thanks for the reminder, Dixie and Ray!

Gentle Reflections: If someone is not familiar with the dying process, it will be more difficult for them to understand the needs and concerns of their dying loved one and to know what to expect. Most often the dying loved one weakens to the point where their caregiver must provide all their care. Even the ability to swallow, roll over in bed or keep their eyes open often diminishes. Being aware of future needs will empower the caregiver to provide the best care for their loved one and reduce the fear and anxiety associated with death.

Grace

Grace!   What a beautiful thing and what a beautiful name! My grandmother's name was Grace; I, Judy, was her granddaughter.

She was a beautiful woman about five feet tall with wavy white hair. She carried just the right amount of plumpness. The only time Grandma wasn't beautiful outside was when she had removed her teeth! Fortunately, I only saw her once like that but that was enough. A young child sure can be frightened by the unknown.

Years later, when Grandma was very sick with congestive heart failure (CHF), she stayed in the home of my Aunt Donnamae and Uncle Bob. Grandma's bed was set up in the living room where she could view the daily activities of living. The tv, the birds outside the window, the busy city street and the front door were all within her line of vision. I know Grandma had lots of joy around her then because our family is a jolly family most of the time. We could find humor in a toilet backing up! So even Grandma's dying had joy and laughter surrounding it as well as lots of sorrow.

Several joyful moments come to mind about those days when Grandma was so sick. Aunt Donnamae can tell them the best as she was there constantly by Grandma's side: "I was giving her a bath in the tub, she looked at me and said, 'Just look at my boobs; the older I get the lower they hang!'" (Grandma would have never said "boob" in front of anyone!)

Toward the end of Grandma's life, she often got the time confused and would end up eating breakfast for dinner. It didn't matter then and it doesn't matter today. If someone were to order dessert first from the menu, would they refuse to serve it? I think not! Our loved ones need those same choices when food just doesn't have the same appeal as it did prior to their illness.

Grandma's daughters, Donnamae and Shirley, were both at her side when she died. Grandma peacefully closed her eyes and took her last breath while her two precious daughters stood on either side holding her hands. That was their final wish…that these three women… my grandmother, my mother and my aunt, would be together in Grandma's final moment.

<u>Gentle Reflections</u>: Most would agree that a cheerful heart is good medicine. So carry a look of joy when appropriate but don't be afraid or shy about shedding tears when not. My family definitely would agree.

Newman's Biggest Fan

Joe and Marg had spent most of their lives in New England where they married and raised their children. That's where Marg had been diagnosed with breast cancer and thankfully recovered well. After retiring and moving to Central Florida, Marg developed terminal lung cancer. Ultimately, she and her husband had decided it was time to ask for the help of their local hospice. So Judy visited them in their home as Marg had started to decline and Joe was in need of support.

While visiting at the bedside with Marg, Joe leaned over the side-rail to kiss her.
"Hello, Beautiful!" Joe said.

Just then Marg stretched forth her right hand toward the foot of the bed where no one stood.

"Who are you reaching for, Marg?" I asked.

"Paul Newman!" Marg answered firmly.

Joe and their son chuckled. Joe said, "I'm her Jackie Gleason, not Paul Newman!" Then Joe patted his Gleason-like tummy. Marg is Paul Newman's biggest fan, I soon discovered. We all chuckled, knowing that humor was what would help sustain us in these final few days with Marg, even if it was aimed at someone's jolly physique.

<u>Gentle Reflections</u>: An extreme sadness can accompany the awareness of an approaching death. So it is important to balance those moments with joy. Remind yourself that you probably cannot control how much longer life lasts but you can control how much laughter can be found in living.

Reagan's Favorite

President Ronald Reagan described to a tee how our attitude in approaching an overwhelming situation could really turn out to be something very grand and glorious if we take the time to find those qualities. The following is one of Ronald Reagan's favorite stories, as told to Michael K. Deaver, in *A Different Drummer: My Thirty Years With Ronald Reagan.*

A young couple has a pair of twin boys, both seven years old. One boy is a hopeless optimist, the other a brooding pessimist. A shrink is brought in to conduct a thorough analysis. He takes the pessimist to a room filled with the latest and greatest toys. When he opens the door and tells the child that all the toys are his, the boy begins to sob uncontrollably. "What's wrong?" the shrink asks. "These toys will surely break someday," the boy answers. "Then what'll I do?"

Next, the optimistic twin is taken to a decaying barn. The psychiatrist opens the barn doors, revealing a two-story pile of fresh, steaming manure. Undeterred, the kid grabs a shovel and starts digging away with a mile-wide smile on his face. The doctor can't believe it and asks what he's doing. "Well, with all this manure," the boy says, still smiling, "I figure there's gotta be a pony in here somewhere."

Gentle Reflections: Is it a coincidence that this story from Ronald Reagan could easily be an analogy from the bedside of the dying? Even though life's challenges and burdens may be great, the blessings and joy found in those challenges and burdens may be just as great, if not greater.

Dying with Joy and Sorrow

Chapter Eight

The Power of Pets

Pet therapy is not a new idea but simply a fairly new term describing the positive effects, emotionally and physically, that animals have on our health. Because loneliness can be a detriment to our health, the power of companionship that a pet provides is very beneficial and can even lower one's blood pressure. Not only do pets ease loneliness, they provide a sense of responsibility and purpose for our rising in the morning and walking in the afternoon.

During the dying process, a pet's behavior often changes as the health of their owner declines. A dog, cat or other pet that normally spends every moment at the side of the one that cares for him may now avoid the owner entirely. However, the most common reaction is the pet staying very close, often lying on the owner's lap or in their bed, leaving only briefly for food or an "outdoor break."

The following stories depict human and animal responses in various situations of living and dying.

Breaking the Rules

Carol Izquierdo is a nurse who recognized pets as being an integral part in our patient's comfort and care. She knew how important one dog in particular was to allowing her patient to "let go."

Many years ago, before the popularization of the term pet therapy, I was working in a hospital caring for an elderly lady who was dying. She had no family, only a small dog. While caring for her, I discovered her concern about her little dog.

The hospital rules did not allow animals to visit. With the help of a co-worker and the lady's friend we were able to sneak the dog in through the window. Thankfully she was on the ground floor. We opened the window and brought the dog in and placed the dog on the bed with her. She was very happy and smiled. This made her feel much more at ease. This lady passed away a few days later. What a blessing to her that we were able to comfort her this way. Sometimes breaking the rules is not a bad thing.

<u>Gentle Reflections</u>: Many pets become very possessive of their owners who are approaching death. It is common for a stranger in the home to be growled at when nearing the pet's owner. This is the pet's way of exhibiting territorial rights to the loved one. When a pet is separated from his owner, it can grieve in ways similar to humans. What a clever and caring way these ladies rejoined "best friends" before it was too late.

The Sensitivity of Pets

During one of her hospice visits, Marge Chell, a nurse, witnessed the response of a very devoted dog at the time of the owner's death The following occurrence is very common in loving pets of all kinds.

Mrs. B lived with her daughter, two grandchildren and their dog Skip. Skip was almost always at Mrs. B's side or lying with her in bed. As her condition declined, Skip became even more devoted to her.

When I arrived to visit one day, it was evident that Mrs. B was dying, probably in an hour or so. I sat with her and her daughter. Skip was not on her bed and her daughter remarked how unusual this was. Skip was peeking around Mrs. B's bed as she was dying. At the moment she took her last breath, Skip started to bark, looked up and ran down the hallway, always looking up.

Mrs. B's daughter and I believed that Skip saw her spirit leave her body and tried to follow it. He then returned, jumped up on the bed and laid next to her body.

Gentle Reflections: Those who study spirituality feel there is another dimension that is rarely seen or experienced by humans. Newborn babies may follow something with their eyes and react to things that others don't see. Perhaps some animals see with newborn eyes as Skip did.

The Hummingbird

Helen Disch portrays the beauty and peace that can be found in a little bird that perhaps is an angel.

Jonathan Tatro was only thirty-three when he passed. He had many friends and was loved. His mother Trina told me a story about his friend named Pat, who found a near-frozen hummingbird in the garden, prior to her death from ovarian cancer. She brought it inside her house, cupped it in her hands and warmed it up. The bird flew around the room and out the door. Then it returned one more time to her hand and flew off forever

During the last three weeks of Jonathan's life, a hummingbird came to the window and it kept returning even though there was no food. His mother Trina then put out a hummingbird feeder for them. Soon more hummingbirds came at all times of the day and Jonathan would watch them from his bed. They thought the hummingbirds were angels and that one of them was Pat.

On April 30, 2003, Jonathan's father John stated that just thirty seconds before he passed, his eyes opened wide and his face was glowing. "Maybe his spirit is now with the hummingbirds," his mother said. She will continue to feed them.

Gentle Reflections: Often patients and family convey similar stories like Jonathan's. A yellow butterfly, an owl, an egret, a cardinal and a white dove have been frequent visitors outside various homes of those approaching death. A sense of awe and peace is felt when these same creatures visit soon after their loved one dies.

The Deer and the Dogs

This story was told to hospice nurse Kate Ryan by Bob Billups. Bob had moved his mother to his home in rural Flagler County to provide better care for her when she became ill.

One night Bob heard his Mother call out. It was the middle of the night and Bob saw his mother gazing out the window. She said, "Look son!" Outside her window were four deer grazing on the grass with the light of the moon shining on them. Bob's two German Shepard dogs (Marty and Major) were lying down beside the deer with their heads resting on their paws. Bob's mother said, "See, son, that is how it will be when I get to Heaven. The lion will lie down with the lamb."

Bob said the dogs stayed beside the window the whole time his mother was there at his place where they could see her.

Gentle Reflections: Patients of all faiths draw comfort when they envision an event that coincides with scriptures from their Bible. In this story we are reminded of the scriptures in Isaiah where the Bible speaks of the animals being at peace with one another. This is a blessing for the dying because a sense of comfort and reassurance in their faith is felt.

Arnie, Anne and Booter

For those of you who have never experienced a loved one dying from cancer, this story of Anne Buell Bashista will help you understand what the patient and their loved ones, including their pets, endure...the happy and the sad.

Arnie was diagnosed in March 1995 with pancreatic cancer. Arnie's philosophy had always been "what will be will be." He knew that he was going to die but he also was determined to live while he could. And that is exactly what he did. He loved to eat and so he did. He held his weight for months, played golf, went to the movies, went to the theme parks, played cards, everything and anything he wanted to do.

In January, after months of trying to talk him into letting me get a cat, he finally relented and I went to the animal shelter in Daytona and got a cat named Booter-- a very opinionated and arrogant cat. He runs the show. Booter and Arnie bonded like glue. Every afternoon they would take their nap together. Arnie would sit in his recliner and Booter would get on his lap, lay across his knees, look up at him, put his right paw out and Arnie would put his hand over it. While holding hands, both would sleep for a couple of hours. Booter always knew where Arnie was and I believed that he knew that Arnie was sick; he was the self-appointed overseer when I wasn't there.

In February of 1996, Arnie started getting some back pain. X-rays showed that he had some metastasis in his lungs. He started losing weight and his energy level started decreasing. By summer, Arnie was losing weight so fast we couldn't keep him in anything that fit him. He would look at himself in the mirror and ask,

"Where did I go?" But he still continued to be a positive person. He went out every morning for breakfast at the diner on the corner, kept the house clean and did the laundry. As his illness progressed, he made sure that he had rest in the afternoon so that he would have energy when I got home so we could go to the movies or visit with our friends. "Just because I am sick doesn't mean that our lives are done!" he would say.

Just before our last visit with our family in New York, we finally got Arnie to say he would go on hospice. (Every time I had mentioned it to him previously, he had said not yet, so I didn't push him. It had to be his decision.) His doctor sent in the paperwork and I told them I would call when we got back.

On Wednesday evening October 30, 1996, Arnie started having some respiratory distress when he was on his way to bed. I sat with him on the bed and talked him through it. However, in the morning, he was weak and did not get up.

I called his hospice nurse, Henri, on Friday and ordered a hospital bed, etc. Arnie was weak but still alert and oriented. She spoke to him about Continuous Care nurses and explained if he had stabilized by Monday she would take them out.

Before the nurses came, we talked and I told him that I understood and it was all right for him to go. He told me, "Honey, don't take this the wrong way but I just want it over. I'm so tired. You just can't know how it feels. It's time." It was actually a relief to him that it was almost over.

Since the Friday night when the nurses started coming in, Booter kept a very strict eye on Arnie and the nurses. He spent most of the time on the bed with Arnie. After he had gotten on the bed, laid down and found he was in the wrong direction and couldn't see him, he would get up, turn around and lay back down again. He was very intense and very upset.

Saturday morning, Arnie kicked me out of the house for a couple of hours then he talked to a lot of people on the phone. The nurse told me when I got back that he had talked to his sons and said good-bye to them. He talked to my father and told him they were just doing some medication adjustments. He didn't want him to worry about us

Through Sunday, he just laid there with his eyes closed. He laughed once at something I said (for the life of me I wish I could remember what it was.) I had asked him on Saturday if he wanted a chaplain. He told me only if I thought it was that close. On Sunday I called for one. When she introduced herself to him, he raised his eyebrows up but he still didn't open his eyes. This was at 3:15 pm on Sunday. Again his breathing changed. At 3:30 pm, he seemed to still be very aware but was changing very rapidly.

About twenty minutes later, he started moving around in the bed, lifted his upper body, moved closer to my side of the bed and said, "Honey." With him moving closer to me on the bed I really believe that he was saying his good-bye. It was only a couple of minutes later that he was gone.

Booter was in the Florida room when Arnie died and they tell me he let out a scream and took off running. Later, when things were quiet, Booter got up on the bed and just sat there watching Arnie for a while. Finally, he went over to him and smelled at his mouth, gave him a kiss, a love bump on his forehead, and then went over the head of the bed. Booter had said good-bye to his dad. Arnie was a wonderful person and I miss him.

<u>Gentle Reflections</u>: Even though Anne was a hospice staff member when Arnie was ill and during his death, she still had similar experiences and challenges of those not familiar with hospice and the dying process. Fortunately, Booter was a calm in the middle of a storm for both Anne and Arnie. Like Anne, Booter knew when Arnie died and said his farewells in the best way he knew how.

Dying with Joy and Sorrow

Chapter Nine

Let There Be Music

Music has been around for centuries, and it means different things to different people. Have you ever had a song come on the radio that just made you want to get up and dance? Maybe it took you back to a particular time in your life, and sparked joy in a memory of first love. There are many pleasures brought about by music.

On one occasion, I had a patient that was a retired colonel who had served in two wars. He was having restlessness and bouts of confusion. I found a 40's radio station on his radio that was playing "Sentimental Journey." I observed his feet tapping to the music. I certainly hope he was having a wonderful memory. The music also seemed to have a calming effect on him. Linda

Oh My Darling Clementine

Helen was 42 and she was dying from breast cancer. Several weeks before her death, Judy visited her on a weekend to see how she was doing.

Helen was sitting at her bedside eating a late breakfast, humming a silly tune! How perfect a time to sing with her because I knew how much Helen loved to

sing. Together we sang our own rendition of "Oh My Darling Clemetine." We laughed like a couple of schoolgirls at a pajama party!

I expect that Helen is teaching the angels her own version now. I'm not sure they would agree to all the words though! Thanks for the memories, Helen. You sure were a great example of living life to the fullest!

<u>Gentle Reflections</u>: Some days when I visit my patients, I feel like I am invited to an old-fashioned pajama party like Helen's, singing songs and laughing at silly jokes while sitting on the edge of my patient's bed, which is right where they ask me to sit! I get a warm fuzzy feeling knowing that my patients feel safe with me by inviting me into their joyful lives. Their pajamas may fit loosely and their cheeks may not be rosy but their attitude and love for living is the best ever!

Sing Along, Grandma

My Grandma Lula was 93. Because she was declining fast, I decided to visit her from out of state. When I arrived at her nursing home, I was worried about what I could possibly do to make Grandma's last days cheerful ones. I remember her as always being very stoic and businesslike. She wasn't at all like my animated dad, her son Carlton, or me, Judy. So I thought!

Eventually, I was lost for words while visiting Grandma so I found myself humming! So, why not ask Grandma to hum or sing along, even though I had never heard my grandma hum or sing before?

However, I did see her lips move in church when the hymns were sung, so I assumed she liked to sing and might enjoy it.

I asked Grandma if she'd like to sing something and to my surprise she said "yes." So, in my shaky voice and Grandma's very weak voice we tried to belt out "Amazing Grace." It didn't take long to be joined by several nursing home staff who were in awe at Grandma's singing. Her face was lit up and she was definitely full of joy! Oh how beautiful Grandma was during those last hours together! Thanks Grandma for those precious final memories of you.

<u>Gentle Reflections</u>: So many songs bring back memories, whether it is "Amazing Grace," "It Is Well With My Soul" or "The Tennessee Waltz!" One of the best things to do for your loved one while in their final days or weeks is to play their favorite music. As long as it isn't too loud and over stimulating, it will have a calming and peaceful effect.

A Sandwich and a Song

This story is a gentle reminder of how cherished our patients become, especially when blessed by our own family. Judy Richotte reflects on how a good fish sandwich and a great song can bind us all, before and after the end of life.

Gail was a small, thin lady with enormous eyes. She owned a home across from the ocean in New Smyrna Beach. Her daughter, a schoolteacher, had moved in with her. Gail had been diagnosed with lung cancer, with metastasis to her bone, and thus elected to receive comfort measures only. Gail said, "I took too many of my friends to chemo and radiation. It's not for me."

Gail had asked for a change in nurses because she said, "I don't like being given lots of orders." I was chosen to be Gail's next nurse. We were both in our late fifties and we hit it off right away.

As time passed, Gail's pain and moments of confusion increased. I filled her medication boxes, did my assessment including vital signs, and then we talked about music, mystery books, and eating at JB's Fish Camp- things we both loved! On two occasions, we had our weekly meeting at JB's, sitting at picnic tables by the river and sharing a fish sandwich. We talked of Gail's impending death, her life, and her dreams.

When I became ill and couldn't see Gail again, I asked that my daughter, Sherri Roth, also a hospice nurse, be assigned to Gail. They bonded quickly. I was so glad and missed seeing Gail so much.

I went to the funeral home when Gail died and met her daughters. The daughter who had lived with Gail said, "I'm so glad you're here. I have a gift for you from Mom. She bought it and wrapped it herself before she died. Mom said for you to play it when you are alone with Sherri and to remember her always when you hear the song."

The tape was country (Gail loved country music) and the singer was Lee Ann Womack. "I Hope You Dance" was the song. Sherri and I listened to the CD on a rainy afternoon, while sitting in her car on the side of the road. We cried, hugged, and thought of Gail and our special relationship with her.

Gentle Reflections: Don't ever think that you will not be affected by a loved one's death. Your tears may flow in a steady stream or stay hidden for hours or days. Then a song on the radio may open a flood of tears. I, Judy, have never tried to hide my misty eyes from my patients and, on occasion, I have had to pull my car off to the side of the road to gain my composure after a visit. The compassion you have for your loved one is going to show through somehow so don't be afraid to let it flow.

Let Me Call You Sweetheart

Daniel P. Klebes, Jr. witnessed the power music can have on the dying, thanks to his friend Minnie.

For many years, I have had the blessing of playing music and singing for nursing home residents throughout northern New York. One favorite resident was my friend Minnie. Minnie was a gregarious 99-year-old who always sat right next to me as I played the piano and sang. Her favorite song was "Let Me Call You Sweetheart," and she always sang along with me in a strong and clear voice.

On one of my regular visits to the facility in which Minnie resided, I noticed that she was not in her usual place next to the piano, or even in the activity room. I asked one of the staff where she was and was told that she wasn't feeling well. I decided that before leaving I would stop by her room to say hello and to sing her favorite song with her. About twenty minutes into the activity, Minnie was wheeled into the room and placed even closer than usual to me. I joked about her grand entrance and then proceeded to play her favorite song. She did not sing along with me but rather closed her eyes in obvious reverie and smiled in a way that I cannot describe. Near the conclusion of the song, she placed her hands on mine, coughed and fell forward into my arms.

Someday Minnie and I will finish our song. Thank you, Minnie, for being my friend.

Playing for the Angels

I had commented to my patient how long and slender her fingers were and how perfect for playing the piano. At the end of each pale finger, she had gorgeous sculpted nails with a hue of pale pink. It took nearly all her strength to tell me that her one regret was that she had never learned how to play the piano. "I hope to play in Heaven though," she said. I was certain she would do that! Her smile was always so radiant when she spoke of Heaven. She knew what abyss she was nearing and she was ready. She had no fear on her face but a readiness that the dying portrays when they are ready to let go. Perhaps she and I can play a piano duet someday!   Judy

The Last Note

Peggy Kuecken, a nurse who provides palliative care to hospice patients, beautifully portrays the power of music in this story.

Since the age of eight, my father has played the viola. He grew up in a family steeped in classical music. Each member of the family played an instrument. In the evenings after chores and homework were done, they all gathered together to play. The boys played the stringed instruments, the sister played the piano, my grandfather conducted and occasionally my grandmother sang.

All through school, college and during his career as an engineer, my dad played his music. He always said it was the greatest form of relaxation, "better than sleep." When I watched him play, I knew it was true. There was a peaceful aura surrounding him whenever he held his instrument.

After he finally retired, he moved south to a city which had a symphony but no chamber music organization. Chamber music had been his passion so after connecting with members of the symphony, he helped develop a chamber music orchestra. One of the members was the pastor of the church he attended who shared his passion for music. The pastor enjoyed the music played in the church on Sundays but wanted something more for his congregation, so he invited members of the orchestra to play in the church. My Dad was delighted. The quartet of the orchestra became regular contributors to the Sunday service, with the pastor occasionally joining in.

Later the pastor became ill, diagnosed with lymphoma. Chemotherapy and radiation made him weak and unable to carry out many of his duties. Since he was not able to come to the music, the quartet went to him. When he was at home recovering from treatments, the quartet visited and played music for him.

He went into remission briefly and then the disease came back with a vengeance. He requested no *more therapy, as he was tired. The quartet wondered what could they do for him. "Come and play," said his wife. "That will be the best therapy."*

The quartet selected the pieces he most loved, and went to his home on a Sunday afternoon and played for him. He told them how much he enjoyed the "concert" and appreciated the hours they spent together. They promised to come again if he would like and he nodded, but it was not to be. Two days later he died quietly in his sleep.

After his funeral, his wife told the quartet how he spoke of their concert and how peaceful it made him feel. My dad and his group felt their loss deeply but were glad they could give back to the man who gave so much to the community.

Gentle Reflections: Dying is not a secret to those who will be dying soon because very often they have a sense of their approaching death and may even tell you the day and hour. Is there a greater way to prepare then to heed their warning by calling loved ones to their side while there is time? Our loved one may even find the extra strength and will power to wait for a special occasion or for a loved one to arrive.

Final Thoughts:

Letting Go and Saying Good-bye

Tending to the dying and coping with the reality of death is an overwhelming task. There is no greater act of compassion or devotion. Finding the strength to say goodbye is a very humbling moment that taps all of one's emotions. The moment of death can literally drop you to your knees or cause you to stand reverently singing praises that your loved one is free from their illness.

As a caregiver, you express tremendous love by enduring the final days and hours together, no matter what the circumstances. Della Reese, actress in *Touched By An Angel,* spoke these words to her husband on their anniversary, "I will gladly participate in the little and the big of your life. But, above all these, I will love you endlessly." How fitting are these words not only when celebrating life together but also when the face of death is staring at you in your final moments

The stories in *Dying with Joy and Sorrow* were not written by professional writers but rather from the hearts of caregivers. The events that occurred within these pages are as natural as the wind which cannot be captured yet still felt, and as radiant as the rainbow which we can see but never touch. Our desire is that you will be enlightened, inspired and less apprehensive of the very natural nature of death and find joy in your sorrow.

Judy Voss and Linda Neider

The following poem, whose author is unknown, was read at Juanita Raffetto's funeral and was submitted in loving memory by her granddaughter Amy Yelvington.

COMPENSATION

I'd like to think when life is ore,
that here and there I'd paid my fare
with more than idle talk or boast;
that I had taken gifts divine,
the bread of life and manhood fine,
and tried to use them now and then
in service of my fellow men

I'd hate to think when life is ore
that I had wasted all my days
by trading only selfish ways
and that this world would be the same
had it never known my name

I'd like to think when life is ore
that here and there shall remain a happier spot
which might not have existed had I toiled for gain;
that someone's cheery voice and smile
shall prove that I had been worthwhile,
that I had paid in something fine
my debt to God for life divine.

Resource Information:

The Hospice Story

Hospices were initially a Middle Age version of a hospital that provided shelter and care for the sick, the poor and the weary traveler. It was common for monks and nuns to be the providers of this care, acting through dedication to God and through love for one's neighbors. The monks and nuns believed that one's mind and spirit needed care, as did one's physical body. As centuries passed so did the concept of hospice care.

A renewed interest in hospice care for the terminally ill began in the 1960's in Britain with a nurse named Cicely Saunders. Her desire to improve pain control and symptom management led her further into her education by obtaining a degree in social work and finally becoming a physician. Working as a physician at St. Joseph's Hospice, under the management of the Irish Sisters of Charity, Dr. Cicely Saunders transformed the hospice concept. In 1968 she opened St. Christopher's Hospice in London, which is a national and international training facility for professionals interested in the care of the terminally ill.

The Birth of Hospice in the United States

Before the hospice program began in the United States, patients often endured hours of suffering at home, awaiting a single dose of medicine which was delivered from another town or even another state.

Then the cycle of waiting would begin all over again. Unfortunately, even with hospice organizations available today, patients at the end of life may endure the same suffering where hospice is not known about and/or access to hospice care and medicines are not available. Thankfully, many patients do not have severe uncontrolled pain at the end of life, yet may have other symptoms and needs that can be fulfilled through hospice care.

By the 1970's, in New Haven, Connecticut, the first hospice in the United States was established and patterned after the British concept, providing patients with the right to a dignified, pain free and peaceful end of life if at all possible. Fortunately, today, the United States has over 3,000 hospices. For example, Florida has 40 plus, Georgia 90 plus, New York 54 plus and California 185 plus.

On November 29, 2001, President George W. Bush proclaimed November as National Hospice Month. The purpose of his declaration was to bring an awareness to the over 3,000 hospices in our nation and to those that serve in them, as well as to those who care for their loved ones as they approach their end of life.

The Goal of Hospice

Nearly everyone would prefer to die in their own home with their loved ones around them, being as alert and pain-free as possible. So what hospice strives for is to provide end-of-life care that is personalized, dignified, and compassionate for all patients and their loved ones, while surrounded by the people and things dear to them. Whether the patient and family need medical, social, spiritual or emotional support, hospice works with a team of support staff to fulfill each need.

To achieve their goal, hospice relies on a team of registered and licensed nurses, home health aides, social workers, chaplains, palliative care and massage therapists, physical, speech and occupational therapists, highly trained volunteers, physicians, bereavement counselors, and numerous support staff. The teamwork of hospice allows patients to have their care provided in their home or home-like setting, or in numerous types of healthcare facilities, where medications, medical equipment and supplies are provided and access to therapies, pathology services, etc., may be available. Preferably, the patient has a caregiver that assists hospice with patient care needs and decision making on behalf of the patient when and if needed.

The final goal of hospice is to ensure support is available for the grieving family before and after their loss. Individual and/or group counseling is available to hospice family members as well as to those who have experienced a sudden, tragic loss. Many hospices also have bereavement centers and retreats specifically for children. For approximately one year after the death of their loved one, hospice bereavement counselors will remain in contact with each family.

When is Hospice Needed?

When a patient's physician determines the chance of a patient's cure is exhausted, hospice care can begin if the patient and family desire. The patient's physician consults with the hospice physician to ensure continuity of care is maintained. Generally, hospice care begins six months prior to the patient's expected time of death. Frequently this time frame has variances from hours to several years.

When a patient is referred early enough to hospice, time provides better symptom management and education. Unfortunately, the median length of stay for hospice patients averages only nineteen days and only nineteen percent of the dying utilize hospice care. The reasons these statistics may be so low is due to the difficulty of a physician in predicting their patient's expected end of life.

Once a physician feels hospice would be beneficial for the patient, a hospice admission nurse visits the patient and family within one to two days to assess their needs and desires. However, if a patient goes into remission from their illness and hospice care is no longer needed, the patient is released from hospice to be able to be readmitted later.

After admission to hospice, a nurse, the patient, and the family decide on a schedule for regular visits to assess the patient's condition and provide care. Also, a need for support staff such as a social worker, home health aide, chaplain or other support services is determined.

When an unexpected need or crisis arises, hospice care is available twenty-four hours a day, seven days a week. A triage nurse will assess the patient and/or caregiver concerns, and a nurse will visit the patient if needed.

When a family needs a rest from care giving, respite care is frequently available, depending on the hospice organization. Respite care provides a temporary location for their loved one to be cared for around the clock while the caregiver has some time to rest and recover physically, emotionally and perhaps spiritually.

At the end of life, when the patient or caregiver arrives to a point where care becomes emotionally or physically overwhelming or symptom management is needed, around-the-clock nursing may be available and is often requested, depending on what service the hospice program provides. This is termed Continuous Care Nursing. During this time, all other hospice staff remains available for support.

If a patient is unable to remain in his or her own home at their end of life, a hospice program may have a facility or care center specific for hospice patients that provides continuous care nursing with the assistance of numerous support staff.

Who Pays For Hospice?

Not only do most private insurance companies pay for hospice care, Medicare and Medicaid may be providers of funds if eligibility criteria are met. Co-pays and deductibles may apply, as in any other medical insurance claim. Because each hospice program has its own specific payment policies, it is important to obtain that information from your own hospice. Many hospices have memorial funds for those in need, which are often due to the kind donations of their community members.

Medicare provides a hospice benefit for eligible patients with a life expectancy of six months or less if the disease runs its normal course. The Medicare benefit begins with a ninety-day period of hospice care, a subsequent ninety-day period and an unlimited number of subsequent sixty day periods, as long as the requirements continue to be met.

Whatever the patient's illness or disease, it is a benefit to have services provided to patients in their own homes, not only because that is where the majority of patients wish to die, but also the cost effectiveness is much greater. For example, a hospital inpatient charge may average $2000 each day and a skilled nursing facility may average $450 each day. A hospice charge may only average $115 each day. Each hospice organization is unique to their services and charges.

Hospice organizations exhibit no prejudice and provide all patients care regardless of their race, religion, age, gender, diagnosis, or ability to pay. Nearly eighty percent of hospice patients are age 65 or older. Those with a cancer diagnosis comprise at least 50% of hospice patients, with numerous types of illnesses/diseases accounting for the remaining half, such as heart disease, end-stage lung, kidney and liver diseases, Alzheimer's, and AIDS.

Through federal, state, and professional organizations, hospices around the country must meet certain standards of practice to ensure patients are provided proper care and management. Hospice organizations can become Medicare Certified and Accredited, which demonstrates a high standard of excellence in care.

Medicare information and statistics courtesy of NAHC- National Association of Hospice Care

Faith In Action

A tremendous source of care and assistance for people in our communities is through *Faith In Action* programs founded by *The Robert Wood Johnson Foundation*. *The Foundation*, based in Princeton, New Jersey, is the nation's largest philanthropy devoted exclusively to health and health care. It concentrates its grant making in four goal areas: to assure that all Americans have access to basic health care at reasonable cost; to improve care and support for people with chronic health conditions; to promote healthy communities and lifestyles; and to reduce the personal, social and economic harm caused by substance abuse such as tobacco, alcohol, and illicit drugs. Contact your local hospice for more information or visit the website at: *www.fiavolunteers.org*.

Gentle Endings

When we go on vacation it is important to leave instructions with our family or friends as when to water our plants, feed our pets, pick up our mail and newspaper, etc. We may even leave someone a key to our home so it can be monitored for safety. Unfortunately, our "final vacation" isn't nearly as well planned.

More than seventy percent of people leave this earth with no will. Consequently, after the death of a loved one, families are caught in an emotional and financial windstorm for possibly two to three years before an estate can be settled. Depending on the state law of residence, personal belongings and property dispersal may even be decided by the court system. If funeral arrangements have not been made, a delay in the placement of a loved one may also occur. Distrust, distress and dislike among family members who are left behind to cope can transpire.

Hospice social workers who are highly trained in the needs of patients and families at the end of life, can assist with proper contacts in the community and provide support during this very stressful time. Often, it may involve access to making out a will or seeing to paperwork that has been neglected. Patients may have financial worries and concerns over needed care for those who will be left behind. Plus, patients and families may request assistance in funeral arrangements. If loved ones are in the military, the Red Cross and a hospice organization may work together with the patient and family to contact and bring their loved ones home.

Because it is so important that our loved ones and their families' final days and hours be peaceful and gentle, it is imperative that hospice social workers are an integral part of each patient's care. However, it would be very wrong to convey to you, the reader, that every death is peaceful and loving. Of course they are not. It is certainly a goal of any hospice to help achieve a gentle ending and closure with support from the many services hospice offers.

What Hospice Nurse Really Means

This poem was written by Vernita Walker, the daughter of Maline Walker who is a hospice nurse.

We are the ones they call on, when life, as we know it, is coming to an end.

We are there to explain what to expect, to give support, or just to actively listen.

We comfort the patient with our love and prayers, so they know the end's not something to dread.

We explain to the family of "crossing over," they too, need to know their loved one isn't just "dead."

Yes, we know death is inevitable, we know it will be coming soon

But we tell them of the love of God and his joy, there's no time for gloom.

We note their progress in this journey, and we watch closely in every way;

We report our findings to the family, and inside, never ceasing to pray.

The love God placed inside of us all, is very unique indeed.

Not everyone can bless the Lord in sorrow, not everyone can rejoice in their time of need.

But that's the gift he placed in each of you, to bring joy in spite of pain;

To bring comfort to the families and to offer sunshine where there is rain.

We see the discouraging side of life, yet we continue with love in our hearts,

Serving as "tour guides" to souls that are getting ready to depart.

So stand tall hospice nurses for you are a chosen few,

Not just anyone has the ability to do the things you do.

It takes someone with shoulders strong enough to bear the family's tears,

Yet can speak comforting words to calm the patient's fears.

We are truly unique individuals; there is none like us around

And I pray, in your heart, the love of God will continue to rest, rule, and abound.

May God bless you my prayer warriors and my fellow nurses.

Vernita Walker

Hospice Resources:

American Academy of Hospice and Palliative Medicine
http://www.aahpm.org
1-847-375-4712

American Hospice Foundation
http://www.americanhospice.org
1-202-223-0204

Hospice Foundation of America
http://www.hospicefoundation.org
1-800-854-3402

National Association for Homecare and Hospice
http://www.nahc.org
1-202-547-7424

National Hospice Foundation
http://www.hospiceinfo.org
1-703-516-4928

To find your local hospice organization, contact your health care provider or search in your local phone directory.

Illustrator Biography

Kate Strike Parker, a Registered Nurse for twenty-five years, was born Kathleen Watchman and grew up in northeast England. After moving to Canada and raising three children, she became a world traveler. Her nursing education took place at The Royal Victoria Infirmary, Newcastle– upon Tyne, England and at Seneca College of Applied Arts and Technology in Toronto.

Kate has sketched and drawn since she can remember. However it was not until she was living and working in Abu Dhabi on the Persian Gulf that she first attempted painting with watercolors.

Nursing and painting have been two of Kate's loves and in *Dying with Joy and Sorrow* she brings them both together.

Kate lives in Ponce Inlet, Florida with her husband and cat. She works for Hospice of Volusia/Flagler providing Continuous Care Nursing. Contact Kate at KatestrikeParker@hotmail.com or write to her at the address noted on the copyright page.

Author Biographies

Linda Dailey Neider was born and raised in Los Angeles, California. Linda graduated with an Associate Degree in Nursing from Daytona Beach Community College in 1994. She has been married for 29 years and has two grown children. Linda is the Coordinator/Supervisor of the Continuous Care department at Hospice of Volusia/Flagler.

Linda became involved with hospice services in 1985 while caring for her mother-in-law who had been diagnosed with cancer of the esophagus. Linda was not a nurse at the time and felt she could have never gotten through this situation without the expertise of this organization and became a true supporter of hospice care. The experience impressed upon her the right to die with dignity and in the surroundings of your own choosing.

Linda states her experience with death led her to realize her own mortality and accept death as a condition of living. Hospice care is not so much about dying as it is about living with some quality of life until you die. Maintaining comfort and dignity allow for joy to be as much a part of the dying process as the sorrow

You may contact Linda at lindaneider@yahoo.com or write to her at the address noted on the copyright page.

Judy Fairchild Voss was born in Malone in upstate New York and now resides with her husband in New Smyrna Beach near her two grown sons. In 1973 she obtained her Associate Degree in Science in Nursing from the State University of New York in Canton and her Bachelor's Degree in Science in Nursing from California State University at Chico in 1980. Her Florida teaching certificate in Health Education was obtained through the University of Central Florida in Orlando in 1998. Judy is also a Certified Hospice and Palliative Nurse and works in the After Hours Department for Hospice of Volusia/Flagler, caring for the dying in their home or health-related facility.

She also volunteers in the Drug Free Youth Thrift Shop in New Smyrna Beach, Florida.

Judy feels her greatest education has been obtained at the bedside of her dying patients. Through her many years of nursing, she has gained a great compassion for the dying and their families and an understanding of their physical, emotional and spiritual needs.

You may contact Judy at fairchildren6@yahoo.com or write to her at the address noted on the copyright page.

Without permission from the following this book would not be possible. Thank you all for sharing such powerful and memorable stories!

Lou Arnold CNA
C.J. Baigas LPN
Donna Berrong
Anne Buell Bashista CNA
Susan Burgess LCSWL
Marge Chell RN CHPN
Edward Cooper Volunteer
Linda Daniels LCSW
Suzanne DeWees LMT
Helen Disch LPN
Chris Garden RN CHTP
Gail Hageman RN
Elsie Hudome RN CHPN
Meredith Iannarelli Vol. Coord.
Carol Izquierdo LPN
Susan Kaufmann Volunteer
JoAnne King LCSW
Daniel P. Klebes LCSW

Peggy Kuechen RN
Jay Lawrence student
Evelyn Mangham
Sue Mossman RN
Henri Muzyka RN CHPN
Patti Powell RN CHPN
Judy Richotte LPN
Kate Ryan RN Acupunct. Phys
Gail Stark LMT
Joan Thomas LPN
Joe Tomazin
Holly Van Hoose RN
Vernita Walker
Marjorie Welty
Susan Woodard RN
Amy Yelvington
Unknown authors

Glossary

While all these terms may not be included in this book, they are terms which may prove helpful to patients and families receiving hospice care.

After-Hours/ On-Call- When care is needed/provided after hospice office closes, seven days a week

Apnea- A temporary pause/hesitation in breathing

Ascites- Accumulation of fluid inside the abdomen

ATC- Around the clock, which often refers to medication administration or nursing care

Bereavement- State of mourning/sadness/sorrow after a loss

Blood Pressure- Measure of pressure of blood against artery walls

BTP- Break through pain; pain that occurs despite administration of routine pain medication

Caregiver- a person who takes care of someone who is ill

Chaplain- A clergyman who serves religious/spiritual needs of a patient and family

CHPN- Certified Hospice and Palliative Nurse

Coma- A state of unconsciousness, with varying degrees of response

Commode- A portable toilet

Continuous Care- Around the clock nursing

DNR- Do Not Resuscitate

Drug tolerance- A reduction in normal response/effectiveness from a drug

Dyspnea- Difficulty breathing

Edema- Fluid accumulation in body tissues

Foley catheter- A hollow tube placed in the bladder to drain urine out of the body

Guided imagery- Imagining positive images and desired outcomes, alone or with practitioner assistance

Healing Touch- Energy based approach for healing by bringing one's energy back into balance

Holistic- Total patient care involving physical, social, emotional, spiritual and economic needs

Hospice care- Care provided a terminally ill patient by an interdisciplinary team, focusing on physical, emotional, social, economic and spiritual needs

Hospice Care Center- A health care facility designed specifically for 24 hour nursing care given at the end of life

Imminent death- A death that is soon to occur, possibly within hours to two to three days

Incontinence- Involuntary passage of bodily fluids such as urine and feces

Letting go- The willingness to accept that death is inevitable and prepare for it, if possible

Life review- Recalling the past

Living Will- A document stating one's desire for or against the use of life-sustaining medical care

LPN- Licensed Practical Nurse

Lymphoma- Tumor of the lymph nodes

Massage- Stroking/ kneading/applying pressure to one's body through the use of hands

Medical Equipment- Supplies that provide comfort and ease of care, ex. hospital bed, wheel chair, commode, oxygen equipment, etc.

Metastasis- Disease transfer from one body part to another

Morphine Sulfate- Medication used to ease pain and respiratory distress

Mottling- Skin changes with blotchy appearance due to decreased circulation

Nasal cannula- A hollow tube that is connected to
  oxygen tanks or a machine which provides
  oxygen to a patient through their nose openings
Nausea- Queasy, upset stomach
Nebulizer- Converts liquid medicines into a fine mist
  spray to be inhaled/breathed in
Palliative care- Care given to bring comfort and ease
  symptoms, such as pain
Port or port-a-cath- An implanted device that allows
  access for medications to be administered
Power of Attorney- A person assigned to make legal
  decisions on someone's behalf, if needed
Primary Nurse- A nurse that visits a hospice patient
  usually on a scheduled basis
PRN- Whenever necessary or as needed
Pump- A machine that continually administers
  fluids/medications directly into the patient
Respite Care- Temporary care of a patient, allowing
  family or caregiver a needed rest
RN- Registered Nurse
Social Worker- Assesses patient and family needs
  outside of nursing
Symptom Management- Plan of care to alleviate a
  condition causing distress
Tapotement- A rapid and repeated tapping on the
  chest with hands to loosen mucus in air
  passages to ease breathing
Terminal Restlessness- Anxiety/restlessness
  frequently exhibited in patients at the end of life
Toothette- A sponge-like swab for cleaning one's
  mouth
Vital Signs- Measure of blood pressure, pulse,
  respiration and/or temperature

Suggested Readings

*Brehony, Kathleen A., **Ordinary Grace.** Riverhead Books/Penguin Putnam, Inc. 1999*

Callanan, Maggie and Kelley, Patricia, **Final Gifts.** Bantam Book 1997

Coleman, William L., **When Someone You Love Dies.** Augsburg Fortress, 1994

Deaver, Michael K., **A Different Drummer: My Thirty Years With Ronald Reagan.** Harper Collins Publisher, Inc. 2001

De Hennezel, Marie, **Intimate Death: How The Dying Teach Us How to Live.** Alfred A. Knopf, Inc. 1997

Duda, Deborah**, A Guide to Dying at Home with Dignity.** Aurora Press 1987

Fearheiley, Don, **Angels Among Us: Amazing True Stories of Ordinary People Helped by Extraordinary Beings.** Avon Books, Inc. 1993

Johnson, Elizabeth A., **As Someone Dies.** Hay House 1995

Levine, Stephen, **A Year to Live: How to Live This Year As If It Were Your Last.** Bell Tower 1997

Lucado, Max, **Grace for the Moment.** J. Countryman 2000

Lung, Judith, ***The Angels of God: Understanding the Bible***. New City Press 1997

Morris, Virginia, ***Talking About Death Won't Kill You***. Workman Publishing Co. 2001

Nuland, Dr. Sherwin, ***How We Die: Reflections on Life's Final Chapter.*** Alfred A. Knopf 1994

Palmer, Greg, ***Death: The Trip of a Lifetime***. San Fran Harper Collins 1993

Rasberry, Salli and Carole Rae Watanabe, **The Art of Dying.** Celestial Arts 2001

Reese, Della***, Angels Along The Way: My Life With Help From Above***. Berkeley Pub. Co.1997

Singh, Kathleen D., ***The Grace in Dying: How We Are Transformed Spiritually As We Die***. San Fran Harper Collin 1998

Sparrow, G.Scott, ***I Am With You Always: True Stories of Encounters with Jesus***. Bantom Book 1995

Webb, Marilyn, ***The Good Death: The New American Search to Reshape the End of Life.***. NY Doubleday 1999

Sharing Your Stories

If you would like to respond to any stories within the pages of **Dying With Joy and Sorrow: True Stories from the Bedside of the Dying**, we would love to hear from you. Perhaps you have a story you feel may inspire other patients, caregivers and loved ones and would like it considered for publication in the next edition. If so, please send your story or response to:

E-O-L Publishing
Re. Dying with Joy and Sorrow
P.O. Box 1341
New Smyrna Beach, FL 32170

fairchildren6@yahoo.com
http://www.eolpublishing.com
…learning to live at the end-of-life

Without those who opened their hearts and homes, this book would not be possible. Thank you for your honesty and concern for others by sharing your most personal stories!

Dying With Joy and Sorrow

<u>Postal Orders:</u>
E-O-L Publishing
P.O. Box 1341
New Smyrna Beach, FL 32170

http://www.eolpublishing.com

Name:_____

Address:_____

City:_____ State:_____ Zip:_____

Telephone: _____

Email: _____

Cost per book: $18.75

Sales tax: _____
   *Please add 6.5% for books shipped to Florida address

U.S. only shipping and handling: $4.00

Total: _____

Checks only accepted